Summary Bun  & Healing | R Publishing: Includes Summary of Martin Luther & Summary of Medical Medium Thyroid Healing

By: Eric Metaxas

Proudly Brought to you by:

Legal & Disclaimer

3

provided by this guide. This disclaimer applies to any damages or injury caused by the use and application, whether directly or indirectly, of any advice or information presented, whether for breach of contract, tort, negligence, personal injury, criminal intent, or under any other cause of action.

You agree to accept all risks of using the information presented inside this book. You need to consult a professional medical practitioner in order to ensure you are both able and healthy enough to participate in this program.

Table of Contents

The Book at a Glance

Many books and biographies have been written about Martin Luther, but none has really brought an engaging and understandable dimension to the life and times of this singularly complex and weighty individual, and the period in which he lived. Eric Metaxas provides a convenient chronological sequence to Luther's life, and deftly weaves in the key people who contributed to it. Just as interesting as the people presented in this book, the author describes the places that Luther frequented as if these, too, were characters that had crucial roles to play in the revolution that Martin Luther started.

Chapter one systematically shoots down the major myths surrounding Martin Luther especially those surrounding his childhood and how Luther's "95 Theses" were initially spread.

Chapters Two through Four describes Luther's transition from a reluctant lawyer-to-be to an accomplished monk/professor whose knowledge of the Bible was unparalleled in the Augustinian order of the Roman Catholic faith.

Chapters Five and Six discusses Luther's awakening to the "truths" about Christian faith, his doubts about the papacy and Roman Catholicism itself, and how he believes faith and salvation are intertwined. He "posts" his historical 95 Theses, not aware that he is about to set off, not only a series of harrowing incidents in his monastery and the papacy in Rome, but the most significant upheaval in Western Culture since the Black Death.

Chapters Seven through Nine provide a riveting account of how the Roman Catholic Church vigorously responds, not without doses of treachery and vileness. Luther is surprised at how widely and quickly his 95 Theses spread not only throughout Germany, but the Holy Roman Empire.

Chapters ten and eleven describe, in gripping detail, the final official reckoning between Luther and the Roman Catholic Church. He goes to Worms, another city in Germany, to defend himself against the charges of the Church. He is asked only two things; first, whether he was indeed the author of books that he wrote, which were critical of the Church and the pope; and second, if he would recant what he had written in those books. He said yes to the first, and did not recant. He is allowed to return to Wittenberg pending final charges and arrest, but on the way back from Worms to Wittenberg; Luther is "kidnapped."

Chapters 12 and 13 describe the "semi-self-exile" that Luther was subject to in the castle at Wartburg. Here we find Frederick the Wise engineered the "kidnapping" of Luther to protect him from being seized by the Roman Catholic Church and brought back to Rome. In Wartburg, Luther is incognito, and assumes the identity of Junker George. Luther goes on a program of writing about the mass, marriage, and salvation, all of which run counter to the Roman Catholic Church. His most important piece of writing is the beginning of his translation of the New Testament into German. However, because of his sedentary lifestyle in semi-captivity, he begins to experience physical ailments which would hound him for life. As he in exile, the definition of the effects of Luther's crusading has found a word to define the era: Reformation.

Chapters 14 through 16 are where the tension, violence, and bloodshed escalate. Luther returns from his "exile" and upon returning to Wittenberg, beholds the effects of what his words and actions had triggered. Introduced are deceitful characters such as Thomas Müntzer, Zwingli, and Karlstadt, who have their own versions of the Reformation, and criticize and refute Luther on many theological points. A peasant's war breaks out and many are killed in the name of reforming the Roman Catholic Church.

Chapters 17 through 20 talk of Luther's marriage to a former nun whom he helped escape from a nunnery, and the beginnings of a family. Luther finds an intellectual and theological feud with Erasmus, while changes in the leadership of both the Roman Catholic Church and the Holy Roman Empire usher in new challenges for the protestant movement. Another diet at Augsburg discusses unfinished business about Luther's fate and ultimately, the fate of the Reformation. Luther's health begins to fail, yet the Reformation movement gathers momentum.

Chapters 21 and 22, and the Epilogue describe the last moments of Martin Luther's life, and the agony of the ones he left behind. His wife and closest friends are disconsolate, and throngs of mourners honor him in death. The lasting effects of Luther and the Reformation not only on the Roman Catholic Church, but on human history are discussed. Martin Luther would affect the world in a way that few people ever did, and the effects of his actions reverberate powerfully to the very present.

Eric Metaxas, whose books have been translated into more than twenty languages, is the New York Times Number One bestselling author of *If You Can Keep It: The Forgotten Promise of American Liberty, Amazing Grace, Seven Women, Seven Men Miracles, and Bonhoeffer.* He has written more than thirty children's books, including *It's Time to Sleep, My Love* and *Squanto and the Miracle of Thanksgiving.*

He hosts a nationally syndicated radio program, the Eric Metaxas Show, which is heard in more than 120 cities in the United States. His show features in-depth interviews with a wide variety of celebrities and luminaries from every walk of life.

INTRODUCTION - Pastor, Rebel, Prophet, Monk

The Middle Age's Martin Luther is celebrated for two iconic events in the history of modern man: the first would be the posting of his Ninety-Five Theses on Wittenberg Castle Church's great wooden doors in 1517 (Chapter 6), and his defense of his position in the imperial diet in the city of Worms in 1521(Chapter 10). In front of a daunting crowd of princes and high Church officials, Luther proudly proclaimed that he was more afraid of the judgement of God than the judgement of the men that he was facing.

Martin Luther ushered in a new way of thought where seemingly unassailable boundaries of accepted human behavior were torn asunder, never to be reconstituted as they were before. Luther's new view of Christianity was one where individuals possessed not only the possibility and freedom of thinking for themselves, but that they had the grave responsibility before God to do so.

Perhaps the most remarkable aspect of Luther's story is that there are many instances in his life which could have prevented these events from happening. First, Luther was almost certain to have become a lawyer before he became a devout monk; second, he was a devout monk that was not inclined towards following every Papal belief, and lastly, if a more temperate and more attentive Pope Leo X had taken to heart Luther's suggestions rather than vigorously battling him, he might have avoided the whole mess.

Myths and Truth

The following have been generally recognized as "facts" in the Luther hagiography:

First, Luther's father was a poor miner, and he was born into a peasant family who lived in a cramped and humble home;

Second, his dour father beat him to the point of warping his psyche, giving him a view of God the Father as a sadistic and glowering figure;

Third, a bolt of lightning jolted him into becoming a monk;

Fourth, a visit to Rome which introduced him to the city's decadence and moral decrepitude was the catalyst that made him agitate against the Roman Catholic Church;

Fifth, he defiantly hammered on the doors of the Castle Church in Wittenberg, shaking the current pope to attention;

Sixth, he fled to Wartburg after his great stand at the Diet of Worm and battled the devil personally including smashing a bottle of ink at the evil one, staining the walls of his Wartburg cell for hundreds of years; and

Seventh, his wife was a nun who escaped from a nunnery hiding in a barrel that had just been emptied of fish.

While all of the foregoing make for good drama, all of them are patently false.

The Madness of Martin Luther

In the course of his adult life, Martin Luther evolved from a pious monk uncertain of his salvation to an outspoken crusader against the world's most powerful forces, then the insult-and-joke producing raucous beloved husband of his later years.

His resoluteness, his fearlessness, and joviality during his later years can be attributed to his discovery that there was indeed a bridge between life and death, between heaven and earth, and most importantly between an imperfect world and an imperfect God. That Jesus had saved all mankind from eternal death, by guaranteeing us salvation as long as we believed Him and in Him. Salvation did not have to be

13

worked for, because it was already given for free.

CHAPTER ONE - Beyond the Myths

Two issues prevent historians from making a clean beginning impossible for Martin Luther. First, the actual year of his birth has not yet been determined. Second, Martin was baptized on November 11, the feast day of St. Martin de Tours, who lived eleven centuries earlier. He was named after this saint, because of his chosen baptismal date. However, unbeknownst to his parents, St. Martin's road to sainthood was because of his bravery in what would eventually be known as the German city of Worms. It will be in Worms, too, where Martin Luther will eventually make a stand of his, this time AGAINST the Roman Empire and the Church.

The first myth we must break would be the belief that Luther's family was a poor miner's brood. In actuality, Luther's father, Johannes, was a successful mining entrepreneur who had grand plans for his son—he wanted Martin to be an attorney. Archaeological discoveries would subsequently reveal that the Luther family lived in a well-appointed home, and enjoyed a diet that was more expensive that those of regular peasants, and that Luther and his siblings enjoyed playing with expensive toys fashioned by the best craftsmen.

Also, far from being a dour abuser of children, Johannes Martin, as with his wife, was a doting and loving parent who only wanted the best for his children. Luther may have been given the rod a few times, but there is no evidence which suggests excessive punishment. Testimony to his strong bond with his father would be the terrible grief that Luther suffered after his father passed.

Luther, however, seemed to go to schools that were more advanced than those of his parents. He was apparently taught to speak Latin, unlike his father who did not speak the language. At thirteen, he was sent to school in Magdeburg, where he met a beggar named Prince Wilhelm, who had apparently forsaken all materials things of the world in order to follow Christ.

A year later, Luther began his studies in Eisenach, where he would remain for the next four years of his life. He stayed with the prominent, yet devout Schalbe family who taught him to make God the center of his life. It was also during this time that Luther would have heard of Johannes Hilten, who was imprisoned for his criticisms of the Roman Catholic Church.

Luther also learned about the reformers John Wycliffe and Jan Hus, both staunch critics of the church who criticized

16

indulgences, monasticism, and transubstantiation (the "transformation" of the host and wine into the body and blood of Jesus Christ during Holy Mass); all of which are issues that Luther would also take on later. Hus was burned at the stake for his crusade.

In 1501, Luther entered the university in Erfurt, where he got his first exposure to the Bible, and started him on the path towards considering life in the holy orders. As a philosophy student at Erfurt, Luther was exposed to a new intellectual movement, Humanism. Humanism was a movement that attached prime importance to the issues of humans, as opposed to those that were supernatural or divine. This philosophy ran counter to Scholasticism, which had held sway in Europe for centuries. Scholasticism was based on Aristotelian logic, founded on the teachings of the early fathers of the Roman Catholic Church. It was dogmatic and insisted on traditional doctrine.

One of Luther's closest friends at Erfurt was Georg Burkhardt, a Bavarian, who chose to Latinize him name into "Spalatin". He would later play an important part of Luther's life.

As Scholasticism was the overriding way of thought in the Roman Catholic Church, the Bible was not made available to the public, including monks. The Bible back then was written in the Latin Vulgate, full of errors and inconsistencies considering that the New Testament was originally written in Greek, and the Old Testament, in Hebrew. The Belgian philosopher, Erasmus of Rotterdam, who would also play a major role in Luther's adult life, translated the New Testament into its original Greek, making it more understandable to a new generation of students.

Among those students was Luther, who was beginning to establish a reputation of possessing a superlative intellect. He ranked second among the seventeen who graduated with a "magister atrium," or liberal arts degree. It was while pursuing his masteral degree that Luther first experienced doubts not only about the law degree that he was expected to pursue, but also about his existence in a Christian universe. He probably had his first episodes of "Anfechtungen," a term that he coined himself. Anfechtungen was a nagging depression during which he internally had to battle his own demons and who or what he perceived as the devil himself.

CHAPTER TWO - Lightning Strikes

On July 2, 1505, Martin Luther was walking the six miles to the University of Erfurt outside the village of Stotternheim, when a raging thunderstorm struck. Cowering in fear, he writes later on, that he shouted, "I will become a monk!" In refuting his father's wishes, on July 17, Luther went to the Augustinian cloister in Erfurt, and took on his holy orders as a monk. Luther was finally accepted as a supplicant at the age of 22. In another irony of historical juxtaposition, his ordination happened just a few feet from where the bones of Andreas Zacharias rested. Zacharias had prosecuted Jan Hus, who was burned at the stake for his part in the division of clergy and the laity because this distinction could not be found in the New Testament.

After 4 years of being a supplicant, Luther was ordained as a monk on April 4, 1507. He set the date for the first mass that he would celebrate on May 2. He looked forward to the day, but it was not without trepidation. It was at this time, he thought, that he would finally come face to face with God. Present during his first mass was his father, and twenty-plus guests that he brought with him to help celebrate the momentous occasion—and the son that he had forgiven for eschewing a legal career.

It would be a difficult night. Luther had a hard time coming to grips with the moment. He had trouble lifting the host, feeling unworthy of the moment and almost could not finish his own mass. At the dinner later on, he had an unfortunate back and forth with his father, who Luther asked if there was any disappointment at all at his becoming a monk. It was a moment that he regretted in life later on.

Trying to Get to Heaven

The Roman Catholic Church orthodoxy at the point in human history dictated that you had to work to gain salvation. Hence, there were the seven sacraments that seemed like a stepladder to this promised salvation. Luther was a new monk who was enthusiastic about his vocation, and more than anyone else thought about salvation, and worked to try to achieve it for himself. The first step was to endure the Roman Catholic Church's penal system - One had to go to confession to another monk, and offer the stated penalty with a contrite heart. If they repented, the penal cycle was complete and the sinner could start life anew with a clean slate.

There was another way outside of this confessional penal system, however, where a Christian could gain forgiveness not only for him, but for dead loved ones trapped in purgatory. The Roman Catholic Church in its infinite creativity, came up with the idea of a "treasury of merit," where the excess blessings of saints and the extremely devout were somehow stored in a treasury and those that were willing and able could access this treasury and bypass the penal system.

The blessings from the treasury could be obtained by purchasing "indulgences," which would eventually cause the theological earthquake that Luther was about to start. Indulgence was documented proof that a repentant Catholic could purchase access to this "treasury" and cleanse themselves of their sins, along with the sins of their deceased loved ones who were suffering in purgatory. In a sense, therefore, indulgences were like a shortcut to salvation that could be purchased from the Roman Catholic Church and its duly authorized agents.

Luther Tries to Enter Heaven, Fails

Not possessing the funds to purchase his way to salvation,

Luther became obsessive about confessing his sins. It reached a certain point that even his constant confessor, Johannes Van Staupitz, the vicar general of the Augustinian congregation, chastised him for *confessing too much*. To Staupitz, Luther was only doing so because he wanted something—not because he was being genuine. However, to Luther, it was like moving furniture around to clean, only to find more dirt as he cleaned.

He was also beginning to see the cracks in both the theology and logic of the Roman Catholic Church on the matter: The Roman Catholic Church did not really provide a roadmap for how to escape sinfulness, but only provided ways of confessing them. To those who assiduously tried to gain righteousness such as Luther, it was becoming a hopeless journey where they would eventually be resigned to the realization that they deserved the fierce anger of God.

CHAPTER THREE - The Great Change

Even as he was just starting out in his monkhood, Luther felt that there was a little something amiss about the Roman Catholic Church basing its doctrine on Aristotelian reasoning and logic. As early as 1509, young Luther was already wondering why the Roman Catholic Church, in embracing the writings of St. Thomas Aquinas, which borrowed heavily from Aristotle, believed that reasoning and logic could take man to the mountaintop of knowledge, but still leave a big chasm between this mountaintop and heaven.

Luther also wondered why the Word of God, as written in the Bible, was not made readily available to monks, much less to the general public. As a novice, he studied the Bible furiously and wondered why the other monks did not have the same interest in it as he did. He also found it curious that once a novice became a monk, he was not allowed to keep a Bible anymore.

The Roman Catholic Church had also dictated that the Bible should be read and understood in certain ways, and seemed to dictate how monks SHOULD UNDERSTAND them. As he got deeper into the Bible issue, he sought for reasons why

23

the Czech theologian and priest was burned and had his ashes thrown in the Rhine for expressing sentiments that were not contrary to anything in the Bible. He would get more ammunition for his later arguments when he was awarded a theological decree on the Bible on March 9, 1509.

Luther Goes to Rome

In his cloister in Erfurt, Luther was a member of an Augustinian group of monks called the "Observant Augustinians," who adhered strictly to the demands of the order. The vicar general Staupitz had asked the Roman Catholic Church to place all of the cloisters with the Observant Augustinians under one umbrella, including those who were not as disciplined as the Observants. The Erfurt monastery wanted to protest this suggestion and decided to send a contingent to Rome to directly appeal to the papacy. They decided that their shining star, Luther, be the one to argue for the Erfurt position and sent Luther on his way to WALK the 1,600 miles all the way from Erfurt to Rome in November, 1510.

His only trip outside the Saxony during his lifetime opened his eyes to the cultural awakening in the early beginnings of

24

the Renaissance. He arrived in Rome, which was a very different place back then. It was a veritable barren wasteland that was still building itself, far from the divine city that we know today. While he saw past and future glories in Rome, he also was witness to the pathetic excesses and dubious practices of the Roman Catholic Church's agents in the city.

Relics of all kinds were being displayed in the city, and those who paid to see them were able to gain indulgences. Relics from dead saints were on full display. Luther, who took the Mass very seriously, was appalled that celebrants in the city rushed through their masses with sometimes unintelligible sermons just to get through the rites as quickly as possible. On his way back, he met Anna Laminit, a self-styled ascetic who was symbolic of people's attraction to mysticism and misapplication of church doctrine. She claimed that she ate no food or water, but subsisted wholly on the Holy Sacrament. She had monks and nuns among her many followers. She was eventually exposed as a fraud and was condemned to be drowned by the Roman Catholic Church on May 5, 1518.

CHAPTER FOUR - A Monk at Wittenberg

When he came back from Rome, Johannes Staupitz, more than ever, felt that his prodigy, Martin Luther, should pursue his doctorate. When Staupitz asked him to do so, Luther, then 29, answered that he would not be able to keep up with the physical and mental rigors that would come with pursuing a doctorate degree. Staupitz, however, would not give up that easily.

Staupitz tells Luther that after he finishes his doctorate, he will be asked to teach nothing but the Bible, and ONLY about the Bible. With the prospect of not having to teach anything about Aristotle, Luther agrees. On October 19, 1513, barely thirty years old, he gets his doctorate degree from Wittenberg. He actually started teaching before he got his degree, in August, 1513, and, for two years, he taught the Psalms. Two years later, he would begin teaching on St. Paul's Letter to the Romans, and two years after that, on St. Paul's letter to the Galatians. He had finally achieved a long-time dream: To study the Bible, and dig into the book as he had never done so before.

Wittenberg from this point on would play a pivotal role in Luther's life. He would not only graduate from, teach, and pastor in Wittenberg, one of his biggest, although sometimes, hesitant backers would be the elector, Frederick the Wise. Frederick founded the University of Wittenberg in 1502 and recruited Staupitz to teach theology. But even with these credentials, Frederick the Wise was known most of all for his collection of relics.

Among his collection are the burning bush (again), St. Jerome's tooth, and a thorn from Jesus' own "crown," splinters of the true cross, bits of wood from Christ's birth manger, as wells as actually body parts of various saints. The thousands of pounds of wax from the candles burned to give veneration to the over 19,000 relics in Frederick's collection are said to have shaved off over 19 million years of suffering in purgatory because of relatives who paid to view Frederick's collection.

Luther's stay at the University left him with precious little time for anything else, including his dreaded *Anfechtungen*. It was also a time where his intense focus on the Bible made him see things beyond the scope of biblical understanding.

While the Roman Catholic Church wanted its monks to understand and learn only what the church taught about the Bible, Luther believed otherwise. He thought that monks should not only adhere to the letter of the Bible, but to understand its message while asking God for spiritual guidance. He understood that he himself often struggled to find this spiritual meaning, until the Cloaca experience in 1517.

CHAPTER FIVE - The "Cloaca" Experience

Even as early as 1516, Luther already began to express his doubts on why the Roman Catholic Church had always had somewhat of a "just shut up, and do what we say, or else" policy. He saw how monks like Jan Hus were murdered by the Roman Catholic Church for merely expressing dissenting interpretations of the Bible; interpretations that Luther found nothing wrong with. How these small stirrings of discontent inside him exploded into the Reformation started quite innocently enough.

Luther would write that the groundbreaking insight came to him while he was in the Cloaca tower in the Black Cloister in Wittenberg. "Cloaca", roughly translated, means "sewer," and in modern times we now call it an outhouse or a toilet.

Luther maintains that it was during his time spent in the cloaca that a paraphrased passage in Paul's letter to the Romans hit him: "He who through faith is righteous shall live." That it happened where (jokingly) Luther said it did meant that the insight was humbling and humiliating.

The cloaca experience made Luther realize, counting his own fruitless search for salvation that we are not in need of healing. This world we live in is the antechamber to eternal death and hell, and we should allow God to come to us in this filthiest of places. We are, in fact, dead and need to be resurrected; and the only one who could give us life is God. And this help is a free gift – it is grace. That this notion of this grace occurred to Luther *in cloaca* instead of the glittering gold of the papacy in Rome is earthshaking.

Put another way, all the gilded splendor found in the Roman Catholic Church in Rome is nothing but a monument to human efforts to be God-like, because the real God is not found there, but is instead in our daily lives;- the mundane. But only if we allow him to enter. The Roman Catholic Church is also in error when it encourages us to venerate Mary and the saints. Because if we have to go through them to get to God, we are denying the incarnation, Cross, and resurrection; and that these were not sufficient to save us - We are saying therefore that God's power alone does not suffice.

Jonathan Tetzel and the Indulgence Controversy

Jonathan Tetzel was a Franciscan friar appointed by Pope Leo the X (really Giovanni di Lorenzo de' Medici) to be the "commissioner of indulgences" in Germany. Desperately needing money to construct the Basilica in Rome, the Pope looked to Tetzel help raise what would be equivalent to today's billions of dollars for the Roman Catholic Church's construction projects.

Tetzel coursed his indulgence campaign in Wittenberg through Archbishop Albrecht in Mainz, because doing so in Wittenberg would be in direct competition to Frederick's own relic enterprise. Still, Wittenberg residents were drawn to the Tetzel product and travelled to nearby towns to purchase indulgences.

Now that the indulgence enterprise from the Roman Catholic Church was right in his backyard, Luther saw with a cynical eye the foulness that indulgences had on common folk. They forked over their hard earned money to purchase the worthless (to Luther) products. Luther understood where salvation came from, and it certainly did not come from Tetzel's indulgence carts or Frederick's relic warehouses, for that matter. He wanted to correct the faults that he had found.

In February and March, 1517, he began preaching against

31

them. He reserved his harshest words for the sale of indulgences as a means of "freeing" a departed relative from purgatory, a concept that cannot be found anywhere in the Bible. Things would soon come to a head, and neither party would budge. Not Luther as he fights against the blasphemies, he continues to witness, and not the business of selling indulgences which the church heavily supported.

CHAPTER SIX - The Theses Are Posted

The "start" of the Reformation is typically said to have happened on October 31, 1517, which is the day on which Martin Luther stepped up to the great doors of the Castle Church in Wittenberg and nailed his Ninety-five Theses in stark defiance of the indulgence situation with the Roman Catholic Church.

The truth of the matter is this: while the theses were actually written before that date, they were posted on the doors about two weeks after October 31, 1517. Much of the attribution of the date comes from Luther's prodigy, Melanchthon who may or may not have remembered the details correctly.

This nuance in the actual date is significant because while Luther did not charge the doors of the Wittenberg church on that day, he did post a letter to Archbishop Albrecht of Mainz; a much less dramatic and benign event. This letter was not even an angry denouncement of the proliferation of the indulgences business. Through it, what he really wanted to do was to set up the subject matter for scholarly debate. That the Theses were written in Latin should have provided a clue, given that very few people could read or understand the language in those days except scholarly types.

It would also be useful to understand that the doors of the church served a purpose similar to that of a community bulletin board in those days. An incomprehensible Latin-language letter would not have been understood by the multitude anyway. This says a lot about who the Theses were addressed to— the only people he knew would be able to read its contents.

The tone of the letter exuded nothing but respect. There were no angry demands towards anyone, certainly not to the pope or the Roman Catholic Church, to immediately abolish the purchase of indulgences. Any person reading the letter without prior knowledge of its explosive potential would take it as a polite invitation to discuss Luther's main point about indulgences: that no passage in the Bible mentions that a person could buy their way to salvation. Never mind that there was also no mention of purgatory in the Bible, and that the Ten Commandments specifically prohibit worshipping images and other symbols which the Roman Catholic Church sold and promoted.

The reason that the content of his Theses blew up was because his addressee, Bishop Albrecht, had a vested interest in the sale of indulgences. Unbeknownst to Luther, Albrecht was the overseer of fund-raising in his territory to help build the basilica in Rome. But Albrecht had another reason why he favored indulgences - he wanted to bypass a law that allowed only one archbishop position in a certain region. This could be done if he could pay the then astounding sum of 23,000 ducats, which at today's prices would be about $5 million dollars. Albrecht was able to borrow the tidy sum from Jakob Fugger of the mega wealthy Fugger banking family. The way to pay it back was for Albrecht to make his repayment part of his indulgence fund-raising activities.

So Luther had unwittingly provoked people with huge financial interests in the peddling of indulgences. Tetzel, the indulgence peddler that Pope Leo X had personally sent, began the fireworks by announcing that "In three weeks I will throw the heretic (alluding to Luther) into the fire," threatening the fate that heretics faced back in those days—being burned at the stake.

Albrecht opened Luther's letter containing the Theses one month after it was posted, and already upset that the current indulgence effort was not going well, was enraged. The eleven or so other theologians that got copies of the letter knew that they had a potentially fiery issue on their hands, and decided to pass the issue to Rome, which finally lit the warehouse of fireworks.

Luther, who at the time did not realize the chain of events he had just started, was just as unaware that printers, giddy with the new book printing technology that Guttenberg had invented just over half a century earlier, found the Theses worth disseminating (for a tidy sum) and proceeded to print thousands of copies which were sold all over Europe, reaching people such as Erasmus, Thomas More, and a not-too-happy King Henry VIII in England, who immediately condemned the Theses and Luther. In today's world, the words "going viral" might be the most appropriate metaphor to what was happening at the time.

Tetzel, who had initial angry outbursts against the Theses, decided that if he would rise to the intellectual level of Luther, he might convince the deluded Augustinian to recant his Theses. Tetzel decided to write an even-tempered response that refuted Luther's Theses. Things went from bad to worse when students at the University in Wittenberg expressed their displeasure with the Tetzel response, and burned 800 copies in a public bonfire, an event that horrified Luther, who knew that he would be blamed for the outrageous actions of his students.

Alarmed by the outrage and controversy that his Theses was causing, Luther tried to write an effusive version of his

Theses and sent it to the Bishop of Brandenburg, explaining that he did not send them out for public consumption, and was not aware of its distribution. But even copies of his subsequent landmark sermon, *Indulgences and Grace,* were made public and absent any copyright laws, as well as they were being sold at a tidy profit by anyone who owned a printing press. The most inflammatory part of the sermon was that Luther maintained that indulgences and purgatory were not biblical and wrong.

Tetzel would not back down, and charged Luther as standing with Jan Van Hus and John Wycliffe, two former priests who were burned for their supposedly heretical views. His argument was that the laws on indulgences were written by the pope, and being the Vicar of Christ, is not capable of error. Saying that the pope errs rises to the level of heresy, and should be treated as such. It did not help that Tetzel was Dominican, an order famously known for its rivalry with Luther's Augustinians.

A frustrated Luther fought fire with fire, and charged Tetzel with not knowing enough about the subject and should just concern himself with worldly things, of which he is more closely acquainted. Luther continued to have public, although written, arguments not only with Tetzel, but with others like

Johannes Eck, a former friend of Luther, where the arguments included other topics, such the evils of Scholasticism, which was a philosophical foundation of the Roman Catholic Church.

The Roman Catholic Church, finding it necessary to finally insert itself into the controversy, enlisted Sylvester Mazzolini, a The Dominican friar, who took the name Prierias, after his town, Priero. Prieras was tasked to examine the Theses and assert its validity and impact. Prieras did not take long, or infuse much theological discussion into the issue. He simply concluded that the Theses bordered on heresy, and that Luther must come to Rome and face the Inquisition, a formal trial which usually meant that the defendant would end up being burned at the stake. This only caused to anger Luther more, and he responded that Prieras' conclusions were without any theological merit and were an insult to intellect.

In the meantime, Philip Schwartzerdt, whom history will remember as the Humanist "Melanchthon," would enter Luther's life, and would be instrumental in helping Luther fight his doctrinal battles. .

CHAPTER SEVEN - The Diet at Augsburg

That Luther would have to be tried is something that had already been agreed on. The only question was *where?* Luther knew that he would face certain death if he went to Rome, so he asked Spalatin to consult Frederick on the possibility of his trial being held in Germany, instead or Rome. His request was made when the Holy Roman Empire was in the midst of a succession crisis. Emperor Maximilian, although only in his fifties, was already quite ill. He wanted his nephew, Charles, to be the new emperor, and Frederick, an elector, was an invaluable ally in this effort. Maximilian was upset at the trouble that Luther was causing, and not wanting any controversy or trouble, wanted to put an end to the movement as quickly as possible. He knew that the cards were stacked against Luther anyway, and the sooner that the trial was completed, the sooner his problems would end.

Even if he was not bound for Rome, Luther still felt that his life was in danger in any other place outside of Wittenberg. In Augsburg, the Roman Catholic Church had sent over Cardinal Cajetan, a committed advocate of papal power to once and for all end the Luther foolishness, who he characterized as a "weed in the Lord's vineyard."

Luther left for Augsburg on September 25, 1517, and upon arriving, met with a Cajetan envoy, Urban de Serralonga, who was deployed to perhaps soften Luther up and make him recant even before the actual trial was to take place. But, of course, Luther could not be moved, and he refused to recant.

When he finally meets Cajetan, Luther tells him that he would recant if they could show him where he had erred. After all, he argued, how could he recant something that he knew was not in error?

Cajetan prepared for this moment, and undaunted, mentioned two "errors" that Luther was making. He said that Luther had denied that the "church's treasury" contained the "merits of the saints and Christ." Next, Luther had said that faith by itself delivered forgiveness, even before the absolution of a priest of the Roman Catholic Church had granted it. Luther countered that the church's treasury was already full, with the sacrifice of Christ, as expressed in the Bible in Matthew. Grace was free, and the church did not have to be the conduit to dole out any "merits" from the treasury.

Cajetan flashed a papal decree from 1343 that he believed would intimidate Luther because, first, it was issued on authority of the pope, and second, it would be so obscure and unknown that Luther would just capitulate based only on its existence. But Luther was prepared, and he knew the decree's details. He pointed out that his understanding of the papal decree was erroneous, and that it was a matter of grammar. Christ had already acquired the merits for everyone, and no further "acquiring" was needed. Luther then invoked passages from the Paul's letter to the Romans to prove that no church intervention was needed to issue grace and salvation.

Outwitted by Luther, Cajetan and Serralonga were left to try to persuade Luther's friend Linck and Staupitz to ask Luther to recant. Instead, Staupitz abdicated any authority over Luther, which meant that any of Luther's actions could not be attributable to Staupitz. This absolved Staupitz of any fault arising from Luther's actions. The papal authorities then agreed to try Luther at some future time. Luther knew that no matter when and where any future trial would be held, he would still be found guilty, sent back to Rome, and killed. Luther somehow is able to slip out one night, and leaves Augsburg.

Rome did all they could to try to get back Luther: pleading with Frederick and Staupitz, threatening Luther himself, and even offering Frederick the Golden Rose of Virtue, a special flower that was supposed to have been given extra special benediction. But this did not sway Frederick one bit. Rome also sent a special envoy, a papal nuncio, Karl Von Miltitz, to ask Luther to recant.

Rome gives Luther four things he needs do to in order for Rome to leave him alone, the most important one being that he stop talking against indulgences. Luther surprisingly agrees, but later on tells Rome that his viewsspread way further than he had anticipated, and that no revocation on his part would do any good.

CHAPTER EIGHT - The Leipzig Debate

As the progress of Rome's case against Luther began to slow down, Luther's arguments against Johannes Eck once again began to heat up. Eck agreed that the power of the pope was the final authority on all theological matters, while Luther argued that final word had to be based on what was in the Scriptures. They settled on having a debate to settle their arguments once and for all. Luther continued to argue that good deeds would not grant salvation, but the biggest issue that they needed to settle was the papal authority. Eck requested that a debate be held in the University of Leipzig, where they could publicly argue their points.

The debate in Leipzig was scheduled for June 27, 1529 with three participants: Luther, Eck and Karlstadt. It was a rare spectacle to see Luther argue his points against two able theological minds. People came from all over Germany to witness the event which pitted a "dyed in the wool" disciple of Scholasticism and the papacy, versus Luther.

Luther's group was at a disadvantage from the very beginning. Leipzig was a stronghold of the papacy. The less than stellar faculty in the city's university had gathered crowds to rally behind Eck, regardless of the merits of Luther's arguments.

The university's faculty, in fact, did not even want Luther to get the opportunity to voice out his heresies by posting placards all over the city. Luther and Karlstadt's students were armed with swords, but this did not prevent Karlstadt's cart from flipping over, and ruining the confidence of the embarrassed Humanist. The debate would go on for seventeen days.

Eck started the debate by saying that the Roman Catholic Church needed a pope, saying it was impossible for Christians to move on and about with a leader to guide them. He brandished various bulls and Council directives that argued that there would be chaos if the pope lost even a tiny bit of his authority.

Luther argued from a scriptural standpoint. He reiterated that there was no other true head of the church than Jesus Christ, who is in no need of any intermediary. Christ rules through his Word via the Scriptures. His sovereignty surpasses and supplants any and all authority contrived by men.

Regardless of the strengths of his arguments, two sets of judges comprised of theologians from Paris decided in Eck's favor as the predominantly pro-Eck crowd cheered. Luther seemed bowed by his loss, and left for Wittenberg now certain that Rome would turn up the heat.

CHAPTER NINE - The Bull against Luther

In May 1520, a Papal Bull against Luther was jointly drafted by Eck and Cajetan enumerating forty-one charges against him, and was published in Rome by Pope Leo on June 24. After the Bull was delivered to the three Saxony cathedral cities, Brandenburg, Merseburg, and Meissen, Luther had to appear in Rome within sixty days to answer the charges in the Papal Bull. The clock started on September 29, meaning that Luther had until the end of November to present himself.

The Bull included a directive to the churches which received it to burn Luther's books in public together with his excommunication. While most of the churches' leaders agreed to burn his work, these were done rather half-heartedly and many resisted as many Germans publicly seemed to support Luther's positions. In one instance, a brilliant theologian Jerome Aleander, now a Papal Nuncio or emissary, who was tasked by the Pope to be one of those delivering the Bull, was almost stoned to death in Mainz.

In early December, Luther, Philip Melanchthon, and a

student, Johannes Agricola, posted an invitation to an event that called for the burning of the Papal Bull and the revelation of the Anti-Christ. The event transpired on December 10, 1520, at 9:00 p.m. and was enthusiastically attended by a big crowd which also burned the books of other well-known icons of the Roman Catholic Church such as Thomas Aquinas.

On January 3, 1521, the sixty days having long-passed, Pope Leo issues another Bull formally excommunicating Luther. But the Bull not only excommunicated Luther, it also threatened to excommunicate anyone who was found to aid and abet Luther and the spreading of his works. The Bull also issued a warning against towns that supported Luther, by threatening that these localities would not be allowed to perform any of the seven sacraments, in effect warning them that their residents would not be able to achieve salvation based on the Church's formula for doing so.

Pope Leo then asked the emperor, Charles V, to help the papacy charge and accost Luther, and bring him to Rome. The Pope also mentions that the power and interests of the Catholic Church and the Holy Roman Empire are forever intertwined, and that stopping Luther would be in the considerable interests of both. The young Emperor plays it safe, recognizing the traditional power and influence of the Church, while acknowledging Luther's growing popularity in the Empire. He once again suggested that the hearing and judging of Luther would not be held in Rome, as the Church wanted, but to safeguard Luther, it would be held in Worms, a German city.

CHAPTER TEN - The Diet of Worms

On the Wednesday after Easter, April 3, 1520, Luther departs for Worms with his assistant, Caspar Sturm. He is given a warm send-off by the Augustinian seminary in Wittenberg, and he also receives monetary assistance from them. In addition, the seminary assigns Johann Petzensteiner, a fellow brother Augustinian brother, to accompany him. His friend, Nicholas von Amsdorf, also comes along for the journey together with a noble from Pomerania, Peter Swawe.

On the road to Worms, Luther is greeted enthusiastically by supporters. He is also given a painting of Girolamo Savonarola by a cleric. Savonarola was a Dominican friar who was hanged and his body burned for having crusaded against the teachings of the Church less than thirty years earlier.

He has stops in his beloved Erfurt, and then Gotha, and Frankfurt, and conducts mass in front of overflowing crowds. When he gets very ill along the way, he associates his illness and near disasters during his mass services to the desire of the devil to prevent him from appearing in his hearing in Worms. These incidents make him even more determined to arrive and get on with business.

Luther gets a rousing welcome upon his arrival at Worms, while Aleander gets a lukewarm reception, an indication of the sentiment surrounding the Diet – and overwhelming support for the rebel, Martin Luther. Luther also gets better accommodations than Aleander. At 4:00 p.m., on April 17, 1520, the Diet begins and Luther is aghast at the gathered audience at the start of the proceedings: Noble, dukes, princes, archbishops were sprinkled among all the seven electors of the Holy Roman Empire, together with the emperor and Frederick.

The emperor's spokesman, Johannes von der Ecken, went to the heart of the matter, by telling Luther—first in Latin and then in German—that the emperor had summoned him here to answer but two questions. The first was whether all of these books, bearing his name, had indeed been written by him. The second was whether he wished to recant anything from them. They made it clear that the questions would be answerable by a yes or a no.

Luther seemed blindsided, publicly at least, by the directness of the questions, and he asked to be given one day for him to be able to provide an adequate response. The Diet reluctantly agreed, and many of them were sure that Luther was truly agonizing about his answer.

49

The next day, April 18, Luther gave his responses. He gives his statements in German and Latin, acquiescing to his mostly German audience, and to perhaps prove his erudition and intelligence, delivered his response in Latin. He said that his works could be written into three categories. The first one was his treatises on biblical truth, which could not be refuted even by Papal authorities. The second category was his criticism of the Papacy and the Holy Roman Empire, and how their leaders were more concerned with material things, than by matters of God. The third category was his attack on private individuals, and how he felt disgusted by their practices. He accepted that all these works, and even more not mentioned, were his, and that he refused to recant even one "particle" of what he had written.

Luther leaves the Diet feeling triumphant that he was able to finally deliver his valedictory on all of his works, and summed it by saying that he had done all he could do to help save the Church from itself.

His final words in his defense will stand as among the most powerful and iconic in the history of Western culture: "Here I stand. God help me. Amen "

CHAPTER ELEVEN - An Enemy of the Empire

The day after Luther said these words, 21-year-old Emperor Charles V sided decisively with the Papacy in rebuking Luther and his works. He finally calls Luther a heretic, and labels Luther's works as heretical. This ruling opened the door for Luther's arrest, and presumably, execution in the hands of Rome. Overnight, however, the emperor has a change of heart. A series of placards show up all over the city showing the image of the *Bundschuh*, or the shoes of a peasant, a symbol that the common man was sympathizing with Luther and that his arrest and dispatching to Rome would lead to civil unrest.

The peasant class was beginning to despise the unfettered powers of the Church and had witnessed the abuses of power and privilege by the clergy, seeing them as fat monks who continued to pretend to beg for money while regular folk suffered. They saw Luther as the symbol of their discontent, and they were angry that their symbol was about to be crushed by the very elites that they were now beginning to resent.

The local rulers grew wary as well and they implored the emperor to give them a few days to try and convince Luther. They were hopeful that the monk would, at least, take back some of his accusations to allow the emperor and the Church to reduce its charges of heresy. Johannes Cochlaeus, an official of the archbishop of Trier, and once a supporter of Luther, had another meeting with Luther who had rebuffed one official after another. Not succeeding to sway Luther, the archbishop of Trier himself tried, but to no avail.

Because of this stubbornness, Spalatin informs Luther that come the following day, on April 25, 1520, the emperor would decree and enforce action against Luther, and that Luther had to be back in Wittenberg within twenty-one days to await his final fate. During this period, he was forbidden to preach or write about anything that further criticized the Church and the Papacy. The emperor finally signed an edict on May 26, 1520 that condemned Luther, charged him with heresy, and warned anyone that anyone who supported him would face the same consequences.

But the emperor, the Pope, and most of the people who were at the Diet were not aware of what happened to, or what Luther did in the month after he left Worms on April 26. He left with the basically same contingent that he arrived in

Worms.

On his way back, Luther knew that he would probably face the same fate that Jan Hus suffered just years earlier. He expected his entourage to be stopped at any time, and that he would be taken back to Rome and face his own Calvary and execution. But fate, or more precisely, friends, would intervene.

On the way from Eisenach to Wittenberg, Luther's group is stopped by a group of armed men, who "kidnap" Luther and prevent him from returning to Wittenberg. It turns out that both of the "kidnappers" were friends of Frederick the Wise. They take Luther and bring him Frederick's castle in Wartburg, almost certainly saving him from certain, death the hands of the Emperor and the Pope.

CHAPTER TWELVE - The Wartburg

When Luther arrives in Wartburg, he has to assume the identity of a knight so that he remains incognito and safe. He assumes the name "Junker George," and no one but his "kidnappers", Melanchthon, Amsdorf, Spalatin, and his benefactor, Frederick, knew his true identity. In his rush to run away with his captors, Luther, a committed bibliophile, manages to just take his Hebrew Bible and a 1516 Erasmus Greek translation of the New Testament. For half a year until near the end of 1520, Luther would be practically sedentary, doing little aside from studying his two biblical texts. He considered Wartburg as his own Patmos, the island where the apostle John spent his last days, as he wrote Revelation, the last book in the New Testament. In December of that year, with so much time in his hands, he would start the enormous task of translating the New Testament into his native German.

Luther's feelings of isolation grew further as he got news of acts of violent rebellion in his beloved Wittenberg, while not serious, it was the unintended consequences of the revolution that he started. His following was growing rapidly, and these people who were motivated by his ideas acted in ways that

Luther himself would not have condoned. Influential people outside the empire, like King Henry VIII of England, and royalty in France and Poland, led the burning of his books.

These scattered acts of rebellion in the name of fighting for Luther's ideas were the incipient stages of what would be later called the *Reformation*. It is a term that would not be used until many years later, but the pockets of resistance to the old strictures of the Roman Catholic Church that were born in Wittenberg would give rise to a much bigger movement that would eventually stretch throughout the Western world.

Luther was itching to leave Wartburg to simultaneously temper the conflagration that was happening in the name of his beliefs and, at the same time, shape and push his ideas forward. In what would be ten months of "exile" in Wartburg, this desire to leave was aggravated by a nagging case of constipation.

To somewhat alleviate his isolation and painful constipation, Luther immersed, or more to the point, drowned himself in writing. He would embark on a prodigious writing effort that would have been very impressive even factoring in all the free time that he had in the castle at Wartburg. He wrote on weighty issues such as what constituted "real" confession, and the adoration of Mary, the mother of Jesus.

From his writings, there appeared to be a change in Luther's demeanor and attitude towards his opponents. Less than a year earlier, in the Diet at Worms, he was mostly gracious and deferential, but this time, he responded with more force and hostility.

But responding to enemies should have been the least of Luther's concerns about moving his movement forward. His most earnest followers, Karlstadt and Zwilling, were becoming fast and loose with Reformation ideas in Wittenberg. They put forward controversial ideas on priests and monks, ideas about leaving the service and getting married. They also put into practice controversial practices in the Mass and communion. The spirit of the reformation was being applied in a way that would have been too fast and too radical for Luther if he was present in Wittenberg. To make matters worse, his anointed replacement, Melanchthon, while a linguistic savant and preternaturally smart and gifted, was both too young and too reserved to take on any leadership role.

When Bishop Albrecht, out of desperate need for cash, revived his relic flea market, it was too much for Luther to take. He had to leave Wartburg and see for himself what had been going on in his absence.

CHAPTER THIRTEEN - The Revolution Is Near

In December, 1520, Luther leaves Wartburg in the guise of Junker George and enters the gates of Wittenberg incognito, staying at the house of a friend rather than making himself conspicuous and staying at the Augustinian cloister. He is relieved to find that the violence that was instigated in the name of reformation was not as widespread and lethal as he had feared, acknowledging that every revolutionary movement experienced tumult at their inception.

What bothered Luther more was finding out that Spalatin did not publish any of the writings that he had sent over from Wartburg. He questions Spalatin about this, who then admits that he was somewhat hesitant on printing Luther's letters, which had become increasingly more pointed in tone. Luther was now at the point of no return, and any action, or in the case of Spalatin, inaction, threatened to slow down the advance of his ideas. Despite his zeal to move forward, he refused to take too much personal credit for the revolution that was developing around him. He rejected the term, "Lutheran", which a growing number of people started calling the movement that he started. He simply wanted it to be called Christian, a desire that was trampled upon by the unstoppable forces of change that he had started.

In the morning before Luther's arrival, the signs of overreach of the reform movement were making themselves evident. Followers of his ideas were preventing regular people from taking the daily mass, and even destroyed a wooden altar piece.

Later on, Karlstadt organized a mass that he promised would incorporate the radical changes that he perceived were scriptural. These changes were blasphemous as far as the Catholic Church was concerned, such as the consumption of wine that was reserved only for the priest celebrating the mass. Karlstadt also allowed people not to fast before receiving Holy Communion as mandated by the Church. These changes were considered outrageous by Frederick the Great's counselors who publicly banned the Karlstadt masses. Karlstadt also banned music and singing in masses, as well as promoting the destruction of religious images.'

The swift and reckless nature of the Karlstadt changes served as backdrop to the ridiculous. On December 27, three men arrived from the town of Zwickau, and claimed that they were prophets that had special revelations from God, foremost of which was that the "righteousness of God" could be achieved in stages, clearly violating Luther's understanding that the Gospel granting of grace and righteousness already happened once, with Jesus' sacrifice on the Cross.

More worrisome than the spurious nature of these "prophets", is that they were able to sway the malleable Melanchthon into hosting them and making him pay attention to their outrageous claims. To his credit, Frederick saw through the charade of these false prophets and had Melanchthon dismiss them. Melanchthon wrote Luther about the Zwickau prophets, which made Luther worry more about the spiritual state of Wittenberg, and the reform movement, in general.

Frederick had more to say about the changes that were afoot in his backyard. He equated Karlstadt's sweeping changes as outrageous as the Zwickau prophets. On February 13, he issued an edict reversing many of Karlstadt's directives, and summarily banned him from preaching anywhere.

This did not sit well with the locals

CHAPTER FOURTEEN - Luther Returns

On March 1, 1522, nearly a year after he left Wittenberg for the Diet at Worms, Luther returned to his beloved city. He enters incognito and comes across two students, nineteen-year-old Johannes Kessler, from St. Gall, Switzerland, and Wolfgang Spengler. As a disguised George Junker, he greets the two students who eventually learn of his true identity during a meeting with Luther's close circle of three, Melanchthon, Nicholas von Amsdorf, and Justus Jonas. Fully impressed by Junker/Luther, Kessler would become a reformer himself upon returning to his native Switzerland.

Finally back "home," Luther launches himself at Frederick, who had resisted the advances of reformation in Wittenberg. He tells Frederick that the actions of Zwilling and Karlstadt were unfortunate and were not representative of the Scriptural definition of love. He also decried the actions of mobs, and now that he was home, he would try to set things straight.

On March 6, Luther makes the first of over 250 preaching events which would continue over the next two years. In this sermon, he lays the foundation of the Reformation –

summarized as, "we cannot die for one another," – Luther asserts that we can only answer for ourselves with regard to our relationship with God. Through Christ, we were given freedom through the Good News of the free gift of faith, and should not use this as a license to do what we want, but as a grave responsibility to be a vehicle for good and to love. This would be a synopsis of the Reformation that had not yet been named as such, but had already gotten off the ground.

In his lectures, Luther did not mention the misdeeds of Karlstadt, but publicly dismembered Karlstadt's previous declarations and actions. People would gush at this first, and other sermons, and two qualities that made Luther the unquestioned leader of the Reformation. First and foremost, Luther had a pastor's heart, and all-important quality that made sure that all the faithful were given a chance to take God's gift of grace at their own pace. Love and grace were central to his cause, and Karlstadt's and Zwilling's imposition of doctrine were anathema to this love.

Second, Luther had unparalleled theological insight. His deep knowledge of the Scripture made him see the deeper theological issues beyond the superficial ones. This insight allowed him to divine between what was clear and uncompromising, and what were optional. Committing sins was clearly wrong, but attaching something wrong to a particular object did that make that object in itself, wrong. For example, wine made people do bad things, but that did not make wine, a key component of communion, bad in itself.

In chastising Karlstadt and Zwilling, he said that the rebellion against the tyranny of the Church could turn into tyranny itself. The Good News did not have to be rushed in the zeal to toss aside the erroneous canon of the Roman Catholic Church. Both sides can go overboard, and violate the gospel of love and freedom. Therefore, above all, love and freedom must be the essence of Christian faith; that faith without love is not only insufficient, it is not faith at all.

CHAPTER FIFTEEN - Monsters, Nuns, and Martyrs

Two misshapen animals, an animal that had the skin of a fish, the head of an ass, and the body of a woman, with two different kinds of feet washed ashore near Rome. It was named a "Papal Ass" because of the proximity of its finding place. Near Wittenberg, a deformed calf was born, which was said to have skin resembling a monk's cowl, and a faint trace of a tonsure. It was named the "monk's calf." Luther and Melanchthon issued a satirical pamphlet linking the two deformed animals to the state of the monkery in the Roman Catholic Church, and admonished monks to leave their orders and become true Christians. The effects of this call had an effect on Roman Catholic orders, but Luther did not expect nuns to heed this call.

On April 4, a certain Leonhard Koppe assisted twelve nuns in slipping away from the Nimbschen nunnery inside of Saxony, which was then ruled by the Duke George. The Duke had outlawed monks and nuns who left their order. Koppe asked Luther to help him provide final destinations for the nuns, as women had no way of supporting themselves in the 16th century. Luther happily obliged by arranging for most of them to find husbands. Among these women was the beautiful Kathie von Bora, who had spent time in the Melanchthon household, and who Luther tried desperately to attach to Jerome Baumgärtner, a young nobleman. Kathie would end up marrying Luther, however.

While they were able to save the nuns' lives, it would be only a matter of time before the Reformation experiences its first loss.

The Augustinian monastery in Netherlands was closely affiliated with Wittenberg vicar-general Johannes von Staupitz, who monks had embraced Luther's teachings. The monks in Netherlands who studied in Wittenberg returned to their country as outlaws and were subject to intense prosecution. Queen Margaret of Austria, Emperor Charles' aunt, was a staunch supporter of her nephews' Edict of Worms, which outlawed Luther's teachings. With the help of Jerome Aleander, Queen Margaret sought out the Reformation radicals who dared attack the Church to arrest them and mete out punishment.

One of these was a monk was the prior in Antwerp who had studied in Wittenberg in 1505–9 and returned there in 1520, Jacob Propst. He was arrested in 1522, was tortured to the point to which he recanted, and was released. After his release, however, he quickly took back his recantation and resumed his preaching in the Lutheran manner. He escaped after a second arrest and returned to Wittenberg.

Henry von Zütphen, who succeeded Propst, continued in the mold of Propst and preached vehemently against indulgences, and was soon arrested by the emperor's forces. Zütphen's was able to escape, after which all the monks in the Antwerp cloister were arrested and imprisoned near Brussels. They apparently were harshly treated, and warned that they would be burned at the stake if they did not recant. All but three, Johannes Esch, Henry Vos, and Lampertus Thorn recanted, although Thorn asked for a stay of a few days to think it over. Vos and Esch were taken to a Brussels marketplace where they were burned at the stake, while Thorn died in captivity five years later.

In the meantime, von Zütphen continued his preaching and after preaching in far-off Meldorf, the local Dominicans arranged to have him captured and brutally murdered on December 4, 1522. The first deaths in the name of the Reformation saddened Luther to no end. They caused him to do something that he had never done before: he wrote a hymn to honor the deaths of the first Reformation martyrs.

CHAPTER SIXTEEN - Fanaticism and Violence

As if Luther's problems with the Roman Catholic Church and the Holy Roman Empire were not enough, he had serious issues with others, who, at least on the surface, were contradicting Roman Catholic Church dogma. The most prominent of these were Thomas Müntzer, and Andreas Karlstadt.

Karlstadt had already lost a lot of ground to Luther, who's more forceful and reasoning seemed to take the air out of Karlstadt's outlier theories of redemption and church practices. He was trying his best to create a contrast between himself and Luther, by appearing to be a peasant bumpkin, and preferred to be called "Brother Andreas." Karlstadt had advocated the destruction of images, including the cross, calling these anti-biblical. He added that all images of creation should also be considered unbiblical, because he pointed out that Jesus said that we must present our "naked souls" bereft of any physical adornments, including those provided in the creation. He also maintained that voices would speak to him in revelation of what was true.

66

While Luther's Reformation was one that he started as thoughtful discussion of theological issues, Müntzer wanted his movement crafted on violence and cultishness. Müntzer had his own ideas of what needed to be changed in the Roman Catholic Church, but he also wanted to totally nullify state authority. As a student at Wittenberg, he was initially a close follower of Luther. But his association with mystics led to his belief that a person must be first totally cleansed "of the clay of cares and lusts." This was a return to Luther's days of endless, but ultimately fruitless and frustrating confessing. He also contradicted Luther's concern for the weak, and attacked people by name from the pulpit.

He had a hard time securing a permanent job as a preacher before he was able to land a job in April, 1523 at a rural backwater town, Allstedt, north of Erfurt. Müntzer was inciting violence, and the initial salvo was the burning down of a chapel dedicated to Mary in Mallerbach. Müntzer was organizing a like-minded league of violent zealots that would continue this reign of terror. Even as Luther penned, *Letter to the Princes of Saxony Concerning the Rebellious Spirit,* warning about violent rebellion, Müntzer was ramping up his campaign to do exactly the opposite.

Invited by Duke John and his son in Allstedt to speak on July

13, Müntzer embarked on an impassioned suggestion that he, Müntzer, was the Daniel of the current age, and that it was him, more than anyone else, who could interpret God's word. Müntzer also said that Luther, the "Brother-Fattened Hog," had to be "slaughtered."

On July 17, he called upon Karlstadt to join him in his violent campaign to eradicate dissenting voices in the Reformation. To his credit, Karlstadt refused to join him, and ignored further entreaties. Duke John, however, could not ignore Müntzer's call to violence. He tried to have him captured, but Müntzer was able to climb over Allstedt's city walls. He slunk off to Muhlhausen, where he continued to foment a murderous campaign in the name of God.

On August 24 1524, Luther went to Sena to preach to determine how far and how wide Müntzer and Karlstadt's doctrine had spread. In the process of his assessment, he learned about the other aspects of Müntzer and Karlstadt's Schwarmer doctrine. They believed that infant baptism was wicked and that all images should be banned. Luther sensed an inflexibility that was equal to the papists in the ruthlessness of their tone and promise of violence for those that refused to conform. As Luther spoke out against Müntzer and Karlstadt, his once congenial relationship with

Karlstadt dissipated. Things turned for the worse for Karlstadt when he was expelled by Duke John from his territories on September 18, 1524.

The Peasants Go to War

The moment that Luther freed liberty from its cave, he had no control over where and how far this liberty would be taken. It is human nature that they demand governments to treat them as free, when they realize that they are free, and this can cause violent uprisings. In February 1525, an incendiary codification of these demands surfaced via the "Twelve Articles," which used Christian terms to take up the cause of the peasant class. Taking up this cause could lead to violence if government authorities did not accede to the demands in the Articles.

Luther, through his *Sincere Admonition to All Christians to Guard Against Insurrection and Rebellion,* argued against violent rebellion. He mentioned that the devil had sent false prophets to lead Christians astray, referring to Müntzer and Karsltadt, but this, and other entreaties fell on deaf ears – a rebellion was now spreading across all Germany.

As Luther travelled back and forth through Germany, he witnessed the senseless death and mayhem caused by the rebellion. When the government forces finally brought its forces to bear against the rebellion, the peasant rebels were routed in just two days, leaving over 4,000 peasants dead compared to just four soldiers of the nobles. Müntzer was eventually captured and put on trial. On May 25, 1525, he was beheaded together with 53 others. Their bodies and heads were impaled on pike staffs, which continued to stay up outside Muhlhaussen's city walls for years as a grim reminder of the Peasant Wars.

CHAPTER SEVENTEEN - Love and Marriage

Luther fell into some disfavor with many because of the Peasants Wars. After all, the Twelve Articles that ignited the flames of violence were rooted in Christian freedom, which the Reformation was all about. Through it all Frederick the Wise took a backseat and watched it unfold and unravel. On May 5, 1525, after the Peasant War was snuffed out, he died. The man who had protected Martin Luther from Rome had never actually met or spoken to Luther. On the day of his burial, Luther gave the final sermon in a mass for him.

To this point in his life, Luther had not considered marriage because he felt that it was only a matter of time, before he turned his wife into a widow. On May 4, 1525, however, he slipped a single line in his entreaty to Count Albrecht from wiping out the rebellion in the Peasants' War. He said that if the peasants continued their rebellion, he would marry "my Kathie" just to spite the devil. Kathie was Katherine Bora, a nun who fled her nunnery to freedom years earlier.

Luther was also still a single man because he felt that marrying might lead others to conclude that since his views

71

on being a monk were more traditional than most, marrying might send others a signal that he was less than devout. Luther believed however, that celibacy was unnatural and that sex in marriage was something that was done for God's glory. With Kathie, he finally felt that time for glorification beckoned.

He was married on June 13, 1525 in Wittenberg and the wedding was attended by only a small number of people. As was the practice of the day, the "consummation" of the marriage was witnessed by his friend, John Apel, who was a jurist. Surprisingly, his friend and prodigy, Melanchthon was not invited to the wedding for reasons unknown. This snub stung Melanchthon, who wrote of his irritation in a letter to a friend. He was however, invited to the wedding feast, which were also attended by his parents and many friends from the university.

Marriage seemed to bring out the humor and an innate humanity from Luther. He acknowledged that the sexual act in the context of matrimony was holy and beautiful. Extreme humanists believe that spiritual matters are fiction and that the only real things are material. On the other side are the "Schwarmers" like Muntzer and Karlstadt who argued that aside from the spiritual, everything else was dirty. Luther struck a happy medium by invoking the beauty of sex within a matrimony blessed by God. In doing so, he said that this was a way of "inviting" Jesus into the human world, and doing everything in humility and respect for Him, whether it was sex with the spouse, working our jobs, or raising children. If we do everything in God's glory, we will redeem in Him.

In the midst of this marital reverie, his old nemesis, Karlstadt returned to Wittenberg, and asked Luther for forgiveness for the things that he had written and said about Luther. He allowed Karlstadt to stay with him and his new wife, and even had Kathie Luther attend the baptism of his two-year old son. This development surprised Luther, because Karlstadt had once vehemently argued against the baptism of infants and very young children.

Married Life

By all accounts, Luther had a blissful married life. Much of it can be attributed to the assiduousness and attention that Kathie Luther put into their marriage. Fourteen years his junior, Kathie kept up an impeccable home and even oversaw their barnyard, even taking to slaughtering animals; and managed their money.

On June 7, 1526, their first son, Hans, named after Luther's grandfather, was born. His married life was now complete.

CHAPTER EIGHTEEN - Erasmus, Controversy, Music

Erasmus, born Desiderius Erasmus Roterodamus in Netherlands, was the most notable humanist during Luther's time. In the early days of the Reformation, Luther and Erasmus were allies in criticizing the Roman Catholic Church's legalistic approach, and its emphasis on behavioral issues and silly rules to the detriment of deeper and more important doctrinal principles. They also saw the larger problem was in the pope's infallibility and the papacy's power over all theological issues.

Luther however, thought Erasmus to be unprincipled, and "slippery as an eel." For example, Erasmus, while supporting Luther's arguments and supporting his call for a public discussion of doctrinal issues, was careful not to expressly throw his support behind Luther. Beyond this, however, their differences were larger and more intractable.

What truly set them apart was Luther's commitment to theology and Erasmus' indifference to it. Luther saw everything through a scriptural lens, and at times seemed to be hovering way above most men's intellectual and analytical capabilities.

Luther's emerging nationalism was threatening to split Germany apart, while Erasmus wanted to unify Germany. Erasmus was also one to avoid confrontation and be diplomatic, which clashed Luther's German tendency to be blunt. Erasmus had publicly criticized Luther's sometimes abrasive tone towards the Roman Catholic Church, saying that it hurt much more than it helped.

Erasmus could not therefore, just sit back, and watch Luther identifying the papacy with the Antichrist, and burning the papal bull. Erasmus asked no less than King Henry VIII to write against Luther. When Luther had a blistering reply to the king, Erasmus was horrified.

Things came to a head when Erasmus criticized the pro-Reformation humanist Ulrich von Hutten. Luther told Erasmus that he (Luther) did not have use for glad-handing, wit, and unity where the Gospel and truth were concerned.

With this, Erasmus published his treatise *On Free Will* on September 1, 1525. Much of it would contradict Luther's own positions on free will and choice. He refuted Luther's argument that free will did not truly exist, but instead argued, in typical Erasmus' fashion, that the question of free will could never be truly settled, in effect taking a firm stand against taking a firm stand.

Luther had couched free will in the context that what a person does out of their free will does not matter toward salvation. Erasmus said that this position could lead to societal decay because the faithful would not understand these finer theological points, and their lives would suffer as a result if they failed to do what was right in their minds.

Luther responded to Erasmus after several months, preoccupied with the Peasants' War and his marriage. At the urging of Kathie, he finally penned a response. Luther argued again that man cannot choose his way out of hell, nor does anything that can make him avoid eternal damnation. There is nothing we can do to achieve salvation, and it is important to know that we know this. That we can be made to think that there is even a little something that one can do to advance their march towards salvation is the most evil misunderstanding of all.

CHAPTER NINETEEN - The Plague and Anfechtungen Return

In 1527, the verbal feud between Luther and King Henry VIII reached its climax, helped along with Erasmus's earlier prodding of the king to swipe back at Luther. The level of their continued back and forth would sometimes sink to new lows. King Henry would accuse Luther of deflowering a nun, and Luther would call Henry VIII the king of liars.

There would be other difficulties in 1527 for Luther. In April, his friend, the pastor Georg Winkler, was murdered, which greatly saddened him. Then, the plague returned to Wittenberg in the summer, causing many inhabitants to flee. Luther also began to experience new physical ailments such as kidney stones, hemorrhoids, and an abscess in his leg. In April 22, he suffered an attack while he was delivering a sermon, and could not continue. And then the Anfechtungen returned.

On July 6, he fell into a deep depression, certain that he was totally unworthy of God, and told his friends and wife that he was convinced that he was going to pass away soon, as he felt so weak that he lay on his bed for an entire day, only to recover the next day. He continued to have these spells in August and September. While he was going through this phase of nearly dying, he constantly asked friends and family to pray for the salvation of his soul. Luther had always argued that it was not us that pull ourselves towards heaven, but that it was God himself. Now Luther maintained that even if we ourselves did not have faith, the faith of our family and friends was sufficient.

After his recovery, Luther believed that the Anfechtungen was caused by the devil himself, and the rest of the year did not offer much relief. Another evangelical believer, Leo Kaiser, was caught and martyred on his way to Bavaria to see his dying father. Tue terrible year ended on a bright note when his daughter Elisabeth was born on December 10.

In 1528, the elector John deputized Luther and Melanchthon to go around the territory to gauge the spiritual health of the residents. Luther was dismayed to find out that while they had succeeded in abolishing the traditions of the Roman Catholic Church, it seemed that all they were freed from was from religious activity and moralistic practices. He also noticed that Marian worship was still very much rampant.

In response, Luther wrote one of his greatest works, *The Large Catechism* that taught the basics of Christian faith: The

Eucharist, baptism, the Lord's Prayer, the Apostle's creed, and the Ten Commandments. It was written in question and answer format, so that it could be understandable and more appealing to younger readers.

Sadness would come back in 1528, when their baby daughter Elisabeth dies at eight months old. Luther is rendered disconsolate, but is given relief the very next year, when another daughter, Magdalena is born on May 4.

CHAPTER TWENTY - The Reformation Comes of Age

The Roman Catholic Church and the Holy Roman Empire were at odds with each other as the Reformation was coming of age at the close of the 1520's. The Empire's energy and resources were quickly being sapped by the war with the Turks, while the Roman Catholic Church was bleeding its believers as Protestantism continued to gain footing. The Holy Roman Empire had decided to suspend the Edict of Worms calling for Luther's arrest so that it could draw on the support of adherents of the Reformation to help it in its fight against the rampaging Muslims.

Charles' forces were able to repel Turk forces and prevent them from entering Vienna in 1529. Emboldened, he marched into Rome to be crowned by the new pope, Clement. Clement, whose power was slowly dissipating, convinced Charles to reinstate the Edict or Worms, essentially ordering the Empire's forces to accost Luther and squash the Reformation. Luther and his representatives went to the German city of Speyer to lodge a formal protest against the reinstatement of the edict. It is from this incident that the word, "Protestants" first came into use. But by whatever name, the Reformation was at a crossroads.

Luther agreed to join forces with the "Zwinglian" wing of the Reformation. Landgrave Philip of Hesse agreed to host Zwingli and Luther both parties to a colloquy at his Marburg castle. Luther left with Melanchthon and Justus Jonas on September 14 or 15 to get to the Marburg meeting, which was set for October 1– 4.

When they arrived at Marburg, Melanchthon met with Zwingli, while Luther met with Zwingli's lieutenant, Oecolampadius. The stickiest point came when they were arguing what Christ meant when he said during the Last Supper, "this is my body." They debated whether the word, "is" was metaphorical or taken literally. After some verbal sleight of hand, Luther and Zwingli agreed to join forces and meet the pope and the Emperor Charles in Augsburg in 1530.

Luther was asked not to attend the Augsburg Diet because the emperor felt that his presence might be too incendiary. Nevertheless, it was his message given through Melanchthon that held the most weight. Luther said that all that the Reformation forces wanted was that they be allowed to practice their faith without the government taking action or offense against it. Luther added that since the Bible orders men to respect governing authorities, as mentioned in Romans 13:1-7, rebellion was not possible. Specifically, Luther provided a list of items that he felt were immutable and central to the Reformists' continuing practice of their faith. These included the end of monastic communities, the offering of both the bread and wine in the Eucharist, marriage of the clergy, and the rejection of the idea of the Mass as a sacrifice.

The good news for Luther and the Reformation was that at least some influential people would add some teeth to a movement that had been to that point based solely on words and treatises. On December 31, 1530, a "protective" arm was created in the town of Schmalkalden, and this association was henceforth dubbed the "Schmalkaldic League." Two months later, Philip of Hesse and Duke John signed the documents that formalized it. While Luther abhorred violence and the unbiblical, to him, of staging an uprising against the government, it was a big step towards spreading and strengthening the movement.

CHAPTER TWENTY-ONE - Confronting Death

Death, and the proximity of death, eventually comes to everyone, and to Martin Luther, it came in painful waves in the early to mid-1530. In August 1532, Duke John suffered a stroke while hunting and died the next day. In 1534, Pope Clement died, throwing the Roman Catholic Church's stance on the Reformation in limbo. After this, Luther wrote the leader of the Reformation in England, Thomas Cromwell, who after King Henry VIII was the most powerful man in England. He asked Cromwell if they could bring the Schmalkaldic League to England and stand up to the church and the Holy Roman emperor to ease the restrictions on those in the Reformation. When Henry VIII put his wife, Ann Boleyn, to death and Henry VIII left the Roman Catholic Church to create his own religion, the Reformation came even more alive in England.

Even more death came with Erasmus' passing in 1536. Luther began his own downward physical spiral when the worst case of gout afflicted him, coupled by a nasty spell of kidney stones. He had to return to Wittenberg from a trip as the pain became too unbearable.

But this pain would be no match for that which he experienced when his daughter Magdalena, who he lovingly called Lechen, died on September 20, 1542 in his arms after a bout with high fever. This death made him change his will, and Luther made Kathie sole beneficiary of his estate upon his death.

The Jews

No one has quite figured out why Luther, the symbol of equality and religious freedom, had it in so much for Jews. In his matchlessly unrestrained and despicable treatise, *On the Jews and Their Lies*, Luther angrily promotes confiscating Jews' money and prayer books, destroying their houses, and setting fire to their synagogues. In fact, out of 110 outstanding volumes of theology and Christian love and temperance, the Nazis of Adolf Hitler used this treatise as some sort of a guide to their Jewish extermination policy.

This stance hurt not only Luther but the Reformation movement. For how can anyone interpret the rest of the 99% of Luther's output without casting a sidelong glance at his intemperate attitude towards a certain group of people?

Of course, he did not have many good things to say about other groups of people, either. Of Muslims, he said that their marriages were as pure as a prostitute's relation with soldiers, and were regular practitioners of vile acts of unchastity. He called the Koran an accursed book full of dreadful abominations.

Of course, his most stinging criticisms came against the Pope and the papacy, which fought him tooth and nail from the day that he wrote the letter to Bishop Albrecht on October 31, 1517. His life's work was very little about the Jews, but mostly about the Roman Catholic Church – the work of a life that was about to end.

CHAPTER TWENTY-TWO -"We Are Beggars. This Is True."

Mansfeld, Germany held a special place in Luther's heart. His parents lived there until their deaths, while his sister and brother continued to live there, both married, with families. Count Albrecht of Mansfeld, himself an evangelical and Luther's friend, had tried to take over the copper mining industry in that city, which had serious financial implications for Luther's brother and brother-in-law, who continued to work in the industry that their father did. Unable to convince Count Albrecht to give up his takeover, Luther decided that a face-to-face meeting with the Count would be necessary.

He plans his trip for January 23, 1546, and on January 17, delivers what is to be his last sermon in Wittenberg. The day before, he tells a friend that at 62, his body is weakening, left with the service of one eye, and feels cold, tired, sluggish, and decrepit like an old man.

The journey from Wittenberg is a journey of sixty miles, and will take all three of his boys with him: Hans, nineteen; Martin, fourteen; and Paul, thirteen. He also takes an assistant, Johannes Aurifaber, and when they arrive at Halle the next day, they take Justus Jonas, an old friend, to join them on the last leg of the trip. When they resumed their trip, the winter ice floes had swollen the Halle River, and made the route impassable. Luther is delayed, and arrives at Eisleben a few days late.

Luther gets very ill in Eisleben, and a variety of ailments, including a leg abscess with an open sore, decimates his body and spirit. He is bedridden and while his health continues to slide, he is able to write somber letters to Kathie and Melanchthon from Eisleben, where he manages to give four lectures despite his waning health. In all the sermons, he repeated the theme that started and sustained his ethos and his movement: God through Christ freely offers himself to us even when we are still sinners. We need to ask Him into our lives to save us from ourselves, understanding that we are incorrigible sinners who need his help.

As he lingered between life and death, people began to mass around the house where he lay dying and awaited in rueful vigil. He finally died on the 18th of February, surrounded by his friends and his sons. After his death, people came from all over the city, and his body was viewed for five hours before being placed in a coffin. They took him in a procession to Wittenberg, where his body arrived on the 22nd. His longtime friend and prodigy Melanchthon gave a thoughtful eulogy that did not shy from talking about his severity, but noted that God had sent one like Luther because severity was what was needed. Kathie was inconsolable, having not been around his beloved Luther when he passed.

Later on, a piece of paper was found in the pocket of the jacket he last wore. Apparently, the last words he had written were: "Wir sind Pettler. Hoc est verum." The first part is written in German, the second, Latin. Translated, it meant "We are beggars, this is true".

EPILOGUE -The Man Who Created the Future

While the Schmalkaldik War was lost, the Reformation won in the long run, when the Holy Roman Emperor in 1555 was forced to accept the Protestant territories in the Peace of Augsburg. Protestants now had status and would not be prosecuted from practicing their beliefs. It would end Europe's long tenure as a united Roman Catholic Church territory.

Less than seven years later, Luther's beloved Katherine dies at the age of 53 after being thrown off a wagon as she was escaping the plague with her family on the way to Torgau from Wittenberg. Of the three sons, Hans became an attorney and an elector, Martin as his father, studied theology and died at 33, never having become a pastor. Paul went on to become a renowned doctor. Margaret, the only surviving daughter, married a nobleman, and it is through there that the ancestral line of Martin Luther continues.

The People's Hero and His Legacy

Martin Luther became the first real emancipator of the

working class. He was able to "crush" much bigger opponents and became the common folks' voice with the help of the invention of the printing press, his diligence to get his ideas across, and his communication skills.

While it is certain that many Catholic traditionalists would argue that Martin Luther caused the Christian faith to splinter irreparably with the Reformation, most people cannot refute that the changes in Christian practice that he argued for resulted in net positive changes in how Christians practice their faith. Bibles can now be possessed by anyone and everyone, songs and hymns can be sang and accompanied by instruments in church services, and even with transubstantiation and all, Roman Catholic Church followers can now touch and receive the host and wine during mass.

One of Luther's biggest contributions to the cause of the common man was the transfer of nearly infinite power and authority from the Roman Catholic Church to smaller denominations. This pluralism allowed numerous possibilities for the opening an infinite number of Christian churches, which was very far from what he intentioned. While he opened the door through which Jesus could come into the lives of people, the bursting dam allowed for many false churches, cults and heresies sprouted up to corrupt the truth.

In this regard, his many critics' warnings were correct.

The Free Market of Ideas and the Problems with Pluralism

Luther was not afraid of these heresies because he felt that the Roman Catholic Church was already actually guilty of them. He also was so certain about his ideas that he was certain that God himself was leading him to proceed boldly with his crusade. It is in this spirit that Luther, even if was intransigent at times, welcomed the fight with the Roman Catholic Church. Freedom was the only way to win, and find the truth, and if argument and debate were needed, then so be it.

In Luther's lifetime, while he prided himself on dissenting against the Roman Catholic Church, he himself had not established a standard by which he could deal with doctrines that strayed from his. What he did realize that it was one thing to debate and dissent, but it was another thing to force another one's belief about something. He opened the door to what in the modern world is called conscience and dissent. He also opened the world to the idea that truth and power could not coexist.

Truth, Dissent, and Power

The issue of specific practices in the Roman Catholic Church is the surface impact of the Reformation. But underlying the critique and discussion of these practices was the basis of truth behind them. The Reformation revolution revealed that there was truth, which was troublesome enough, and then there was the pursuit of truth. Truth was both a noun and a verb, and Luther, through his agitation, had by accident, linked both. The pursuit of truth was considered as heretical dissent by the Roman Catholic Church, and Luther had started the road to making this unacceptable in the years to come.

This dissent was crushed violently by the Roman Catholic Church, but yet Jesus came into the world and did not use violence to compel dissenters to his word. Jesus came not because God all of a sudden decided that man needed salvation, man just needed a reminder of how to achieve it. In the same vein, Luther did not have any astounding new ideas. It was all in the Bible in the first place, just buried from centuries of neglect and obfuscation.

Democracy and Freedom

The modern era of freedom was born when Luther sided

with a view of the Bible that was different from the Roman Catholic Church. It was not only one branch of Christianity that was born, but many other forms and versions spread and grew. But more than the different permutations of Bible interpretation, more important is the spirit of understanding and tolerance of other views. This is considered the biggest contribution of the Lutherian ethos to mankind. In the new American colonies, people of congregations separated by the slimmest of Christian doctrinal differences managed to co-exist and prosper together.

It was in these colonies that the concept of the separation of church and state took form, and practically codified. If either a religion or a government co-opted the influence of the other, tyranny would ensue. This was demonstrated by Roman Catholic Church during 1,100 years in their monopoly of biblical doctrine.

Social Reforms and The End of History

The names John Wesley and William Wilberforce of England; and Abraham Lincoln and Frederick Douglass of the United States resonate in history as the leading figures who ended the slave trade and the use of slaves in the 18th and 19th centuries. These reforms would not have been possible if not for the free market of ideas the respect of dissent that Martin Luther introduced.

Abolition paved the way for other reforms aside from those relating to skin color. In England, there were many reforms in penal laws, animal cruelty, child labor, and assistance of the poor, plus many others that were enacted. Luther's spiritual heirs such as Wilberforce and others took Luther's concepts to the next level in the world of government and culture that Luther himself could not, and would not ever have done. In addition, he separated the institution of the church from the Bible, and let morality and love enter into the secular world, so that every good atheist and agnostic today knows that caring for the marginalized and the poor is the true measure of what it is to be human.

Luther opened a gateway where man is free to dissent against their leaders, but also a gateway where they are required by God to take responsibility for what they do and help those who cannot fend for themselves. There is no more excuse to accept inferior governments or religions, because man now has the freedom and responsibility to command their own fate, trusting only in God.

Conclusion

It is impossible to talk about the history of modern Western culture without talking about Martin Luther. His speech at the Diet of Worms is considered one of the most important events in human history. Many historians equate its significance with the 1492 arrival of Christopher Columbus in the New World, and the signing of the Magna Carta in 1215.

There is nothing in Metaxas' book that mentions the word, "enlightenment," a period in history usually ascribed to 18th century Western Europe's "awakening" to revolutionary thinking when it came to philosophy, politics, liberty, and government. This enlightenment precipitated the revolutions in France and the American colonies that combined fueled the rise of the United States, which put on full display, the influence of protest and dissent during this period: it allowed for the unfettered introduction, discussion, and application of groundbreaking and radical thought and concepts that were once considered outlandish, if not criminal or heretical.

Some historians, however, go further back to Martin Luther's unwitting crusade to upend the strictures of the Roman

Catholic Church as the igniter of revolutionary thought. If a single man could bring so much agitation and change to Europe's most powerful, enduring and immense institution at the time, then there were no human limits that could hold back any revolution that challenged once seemingly untouchable institutions.

Metaxa's book gives an illuminating view of what "conscience" and human freedom really represent. In the hubbub of the proceedings at the Diet of Worms, and the subsequent analysis of the monumental events that shook the world, much has been said of "conscience" that Luther often mentioned as he argued against the failings of the Roman Catholic Church. While the commitment to go with his "conscience" has been the battle cry of many who equated this with the unfettered exercise of personal freedoms, Luther's conscience was not one borne of unbound personal needs, wants, or opinion.

His "conscience" was living according to the directives of the Scriptures. While there is no literal translation of word "conscience" in German, conscience in Latin and German *"Gewissen"* means "knowing". To Luther, this meant KNOWING the truth, and the only truth there is to know is that of the Scriptures. The modern view of conscience is whatever our judgement and morality tell us what is right. In other words, there could be 7 billion interpretations of conscience; one for every living human being on earth. For Luther, there is ONLY ONCE conscience that should be followed, and that is surrendering us in faith to God as Scripture has directed.

FREE BONUSES

P.S. Is it okay if we overdeliver?

Here at Readtrepreneur Publishing, we believe in overdelivering way beyond our reader's expectations. Is it okay if we overdeliver?

Here's the deal, we're going to give you an extremely condensed PDF summary of the book which you've just read and much more...

What's the catch? We need to trust you... You see, we want to overdeliver and in order for us to do that, we've to trust our reader to keep this bonus a secret to themselves? Why? Because we don't want people to be getting our exclusive PDF summaries even without buying our books itself. Unethical, right?

Ok. Are you ready?

Firstly, remember that your book is code: "**READ57**".

Next, visit this link: **http://bit.ly/exclusivepdfs**

Everything else will be self explanatory after you've visited: **http://bit.ly/exclusivepdfs.**

We hope you'll enjoy our free bonuses as much as we enjoyed preparing it for you!

Summary of

Medical Medium

Thyroid Healing:

The Truth behind Hashimoto's, Graves', Insomnia, Hypothroidism, Thyroid
Nodules & Epstein-Barr

By: Anthony William

Proudly Brought to you by:

Legal & Disclaimer

The information contained in this book is not designed to replace or take the place of any form of medicine or professional medical advice. The information in this book has been provided for educational and entertainment purposes only.

The information contained in this book has been compiled from sources deemed reliable, and it is accurate to the best of the Author's knowledge; however, the Author cannot guarantee its accuracy and validity and cannot be held liable for any errors or omissions. Changes are periodically made to this book. You must consult your doctor or get professional medical advice before using any of the suggested remedies, techniques, or information in this book. Images used in this book are not the same as of that of the actual book. This is a totally separate and different entity from that of the original book titled: "Medical Medium Thyroid Healing".

Upon using the information contained in this book, you agree to hold harmless the Author from and against any damages, costs, and expenses, including any legal fees potentially resulting from the application of any of the information provided by this guide. This disclaimer applies to any damages or injury caused by the use and application, whether directly or indirectly, of any advice or information presented, whether for breach of contract, tort, negligence, personal injury, criminal intent, or under any other cause of action.

You agree to accept all risks of using the information presented inside this book. You need to consult a professional medical practitioner in order to ensure you are both able and healthy enough to participate in this program.

Table of Contents

The Book at a Glance

No medical mystery is as common as thyroid problems. Despite various advancements in technology, the medical community is still struggling to find the answers for these problems. Thus, this often leads to misdiagnosis and slow recovery rates.

Medical Medium Thyroid Healing seeks to help people facing various thyroid problems. This book contains all the necessary information readers need to know about the thyroid, while also providing them with a comprehensive list of causes, symptoms, and ways to avoid these problems.

To help readers understand the subject better, the book is divided into 31 chapters under four main parts. The first part of the book seeks to educate us about our thyroid – what it is, and how it serves our body. In chapter 1, we learn about the misconceptions revolving around our thyroid, and why it has gained a bad reputation. In chapters 2 and 3, the author introduces us to the Epstein-Barr Virus (EBV), and lists down its common triggers, and how it affects us. On the other hand, chapter 4 seeks to end this misconception and provide us with a clear overview of the thyroid as the body's data center. Then, in chapters 5 to 8, the author explains the symptoms related to thyroid issues, how thyroid cancer is formed, the problem with today's thyroid tests, and the possible side effects of thyroid medication.

The second part of the book starts with chapter 9, which provides us with an overview of how we can let go of the baggage that keep us from moving forward in our thyroid healing journey. Chapters 10 to 18 provide an in-depth discussion of each of the Great Mistakes, which serve as gaps along the way. Additionally, each chapter also provides a solution to help us bridge these gaps.

Part III is the heart of this book, which focuses on the ways by which we can rebuild our thyroid – regardless of whether it has been exposed to high levels of iodine, or has been surgically removed. Chapters 19 and 20 discuss how thyroid resurrection is possible. Chapter 21, on the other hand, provides us with a list of food and toxins to avoid in order to guarantee recovery. Conversely, chapter 22 lists down the foods, herbs, and supplements which are necessary for thyroid healing. In chapter 23, the author provides readers with meal plans to help them get started on a 90-day thyroid rehab program. The preparation and recipes for these meals are discussed in chapter 24. To complement this new diet, the author also encourages readers to try the three thyroid healing techniques described in chapter 25. Finally, chapter 26 shares the story of Sally Arnold, a person who has successfully resurrected her thyroid.

In the final part of this book, the author shares the secrets of sleep. In chapter 27, he explains the connection between our thyroid and our sleep issues. These issues are identified and thoroughly addressed under chapters 29 and 30. On the other hand, chapter 28 lays down the various laws, which we must live by in order to improve our quality of sleep. Finally, chapter 31 will discuss how our emotions project "bad" dreams.

Of course, the contents in this book are not just for people who are already suffering from thyroid issues. This is especially useful to those who wish to find ways to protect themselves and their loved ones from the nasty EBV.

PART I:

Thyroid Revelations

The Truth about Your Thyroid

More often than not, patients who have been diagnosed with thyroid-related diseases leave their doctor with more questions than answers. In a way, they're grateful for the fact that what they have has a name – that it's not a complete medical mystery. Unfortunately, they are also told that what they are experiencing is an autoimmune response – that is, the body creating a protective response against the thyroid and attacking it over time.

However, why does the body attack itself? Moreover, what might cause the body to do such a harmful thing to itself? The answers to these questions will be laid down in this book in a comprehensive and informative way.

Before we delve into the details, the author reminds us that the first thing we have to do is to stop blaming ourselves. After all, with everything we're dealing with because of our illness, the last thing we need is to feel guilty about it. Keep in mind that what we feel – all symptoms, illnesses, and suffering – are not created by our thoughts or by our acts. Neither is it a punishment from the universe, nor a result of karma.

Instead, the author lets us in on something he discovered throughout the course of his work: that these thyroid-related illnesses are caused by a thyroid virus. Thus, it's not the body attacking the thyroid gland – instead, there's actually a virus attacking it. Additionally, the author also shares that the virus doesn't just attack the thyroid gland. In fact, it attacks the gland when it's already at the third stage of its attacks. Unfortunately, its attacks are so subtle that we hardly experience any symptom.

On a positive note, however, the author emphasizes that we can do something about this virus. All answers to our thyroid concerns will be addressed in this book, and the author even guarantees that we will all become experts by the time we reach the last chapter.

Thyroid Virus Triggers

The first thing we have to recognize are virus triggers. According to the author, these triggers are the fuels, which help the virus speed up its reproduction. These triggers may come from physiological responses, environmental stressors, or food we eat.

To help us identify stressors, the author lists them down as follows:

- Mold. Being exposed to mold weakens our immune system, which also makes us more susceptible to the virus.

- Mercury. The author shares that mercury is a favorite food of the virus, so we must avoid being exposed to it as much as possible. Sources of mercury include tuna, swordfish, and getting metal fillings removes. Mercury can also be genetically passed down to us.

- Zinc deficiency. Having low levels of zinc greatly contributes to thyroid virus vulnerability. It can either be inherited, or be caused by poor nutrition.

- Vitamin B12 deficiency compromises the nervous system, liver, and other organs, which help control the virus from growing.

- Exposure to pesticides, herbicides, and insecticides leads us to be exposed to certain toxins, which encourage the virus's growth. The same toxins can be inhaled from fresh paint.

- Emotional trauma can also weaken our immune system by releasing hormones, which help feed the virus. These negative emotions can be triggered by the death of a loved one, a broken heart, the feeling of betrayal, worrying about your finances, or watching loved ones suffer from painful experiences. Hormonal changes like puberty, pregnancy, and childbirth can also produce a similar effect.

- Medications, if improperly taken, can also weaken the immune system. Always make sure that you stick to your doctor's prescribed regimen to experience the medicine's optimum effect. Recreational drug use is also discourages, since these drugs often contain harmful toxins which feed the virus.

- Physical injuries can effectively wear out our bodies,

and this can signal the virus to try, and take over your body.

- Swimming. The author explains that the presence of red algae in bodies of water during the summer reduces the amount of oxygen in the water, which, in turn, encourages the growth of bacteria. When we're exposed to these bacteria, our immune system also weakens, making it easier for the virus to take over.

- Runoffs contain heavy metal and other toxins which viruses feed off, so it's best to avoid swimming in lakes exposed too runoffs.

- Not getting enough rest can also weaken the immune system. More on this will be discussed in later chapters.

- Insect bites. When we are bitten by insects, they inject venom into our skin, which can make it susceptible to infections. These infections can signal the thyroid virus too wake up from its dormancy.

With all these triggers in mind, the author reminds us that we should not be intimidated. We must always keep in mind that we have the right to enjoy life without illnesses. After all, these triggers are avoidable, and the information contained in this book can help us protect ourselves and our loved ones from the destructive thyroid virus.

How the Thyroid Virus Works

At this point, we are now more curious about the thyroid virus, how we can catch it, and how it works. This chapter seeks to answer all these questions.

The author begins his discussion by sharing that the thyroid virus can be easily passed on to us. We can catch it by simply sharing a drink with our friends, from kissing our partner, eating food prepared by an infected cook, being sneezed on, getting a blood transfusion, by using a public bathroom, or by inheriting it from our parents. However, the worst part about catching this virus lies in the fact that its initial symptoms are so mild that we barely notice it wreaking havoc in our system.

So, what exactly is the thyroid virus? The author explains that this is a pathogen more commonly known as the Epstein-Barr virus or EBV. The EBV is a virus in the herpes family that is known to cause glandular fever or mononucleosis. It has existed for over hundreds of years, thereby creating mutations and new strains throughout the process. These strains can be categorized into six groups with around ten sub-types per group – which explains why different people experience different symptoms despite being infected by the same virus.

The EBV is also known to have four stages. Nevertheless, before the author discusses these stages, the author deems it necessary to discuss the different viral poisons first. These viral poisons are the toxic castoffs of the virus as it reproduces, and are responsible for making matters worse as the virus progresses.

- Viral byproduct. Just like any living matter, EBV consumes food and excretes its toxic waste matter. Unfortunately, their byproduct can cause the mitral valve to gum up and eventually create heart palpitations.

- Viral corpses. Each virus cell has a lifespan of around six weeks, and those that die off remain in our system as toxic cell corpses which can clog up the liver and the lymphatic system. This causes fatigue, weight gain, constipation, bloating, hot flashes, and other similar conditions.

- Neurotoxins are byproducts of the EBV, which can cause inflammations in our nerves.

- Dermatoxins, another byproduct, slows down the

119

functioning of the liver and the lymphatic system. As a result, we experience skin irritations, pain, itching, rashes, or a combination of these conditions.

With all these in mind, we are now ready to be acquainted with the four stages of the EBV.

1. The author calls the first stage as "The Baby Stage". This is the time when we first catch the disease. Since the virus largely remains dormant during this stage, symptoms often include mild fatigue, sore throats, earaches, or flus. Fortunately, the virus is still highly vulnerable at this stage, and can be easily treated through antiviral measures, which are to be discussed later in this book.

2. The second stage is "The War Stage". This is the stage when the virus wakes up from its dormancy. This is often triggered by our weakened immune system, and begins with mononucleosis – otherwise known as mono. During this stage, the EBV and our immune system is constantly at war with each other, but only until the virus senses that it can't stay active for a long time. Once it senses this threat, the virus picks an organ in our body where it can remain dormant until another trigger comes along.

3. The third stage is "The Thyroid Stage" or the stage when people often get diagnosed with thyroid problems. During this stage, the virus becomes extremely active and sends out toxins into the liver and the bloodstream, which also confuses the lymphocytes guarding the thyroid area. As a result of this confusion, the virus successfully takes burrows into the thyroid gland and settles there. Unfortunately, the deeper the virus is into the thyroid gland, the harder it is to be destroyed. This eventually leads into the diagnosis of thyroid issues, which are often dismissed as aging, menopause, or being autoimmune.

4. The final stage is "The Mystery Illness Stage". During this stage, the virus affects a person neurologically, while virus cells which remain in Stage Two and Stage Three continue to wreak havoc in our body. This is considered as the most debilitating of the four stages, and fortunately, not a lot of people ever reach this stage. However, those who do reach this stage experience adrenal and neurological fatigue, which still remains a mystery to the medical community.

Nonetheless, the author reminds us that we have the ability to regain control and rebuild our immune system – even when we are already experiencing Stage Four EBV. Nevertheless, in order to do so, we must first understand our thyroid's true purpose.

Your Thyroid's True Purpose

The thyroid is the gland located in the front of our neck; and because of its relatively small size, we often dismiss it as a gland with insignificant functions. However, that is not the case.

The author shares that despite its size, the thyroid is actually the body's second brain. It serves as the body's data center, and is responsible for recording everything that happens in our body: what's functioning or not, or what's toxic or not. The data recorded is then used by the thyroid to send out signals to delegate tasks to the various organs to keep everything balanced and fully functional. In addition, it is interesting that the thyroid still performs its job despite being infected by the EBV, or has been surgically removed.

The author explains this phenomenon by stating that the thyroid is also responsible for the production of the thyroxine (T4) and triiodothyronine (T3) hormones. These hormones play a vital role in keeping the immune system balanced by preventing overreaction or under reaction to stimulus, or by supporting the functions of the pancreas. Fortunately, the liver has a storage bin of T4 hormones, which converts into T3, which the body uses whenever the thyroid can't perform this function.

Additionally, the thyroid also produces two additional hormones. These hormones, which the author refers to as R5 and R6, are responsible for the messaging and monitoring functions of the thyroid. In addition, thanks to our adrenal glands, our body will not be replete with R5 and R6 hormones even when the thyroid is under attack.

With all these in mind, we begin to see how resilient our body can be. The problem, however, lies in the fact that the EBV also feeds on adrenaline. Thus, although the adrenal glands produce adrenaline to keep the body's equilibrium, it also provides food for the EBV. Moreover, as long as the virus has a means to survive, it will not stop until it has taken over our central nervous system.

Fortunately, there is a way to stop the virus's proliferation. However, before we dwell on the specifics of prevention, we must first understand its symptoms and conditions in order to guarantee a more targeted and efficient treatment.

Your Symptoms and Conditions – Explained

As previously stated, our thyroid issues are not the problem itself – they are mere symptoms of the real threat. In this chapter, the author discusses all EBV-related symptoms, which we have to look out for. After all, these symptoms will guide us in determining the appropriate treatment for the virus.

- Hypothyroidism. We experience hypothyroidism when the EBV digs deep into the thyroid tissue, which greatly weakens the gland. This is considered as an early-stage case of thyroiditis, and is characterized by fluctuations in body temperature, dry skin, and fatigue.

- Hyperthyroidism and Graves' disease are also known symptoms of being infected by the EBV. The author shares that there are instances when the virus causes the thyroid to overproduce hormones. As a result, we experience bulging eyes, a swelling in the throat, an enlarged thyroid, fluctuating body temperature, and fatigue.

125

- Inflammation is the body's way of protecting itself in case of invasion or injury. Thus, when we experience inflammation – either in the form of a sore throat or a puffy splinter – this is the body telling us that it is actively fighting off pathogens like the EBV.

- Thyroid nodules, cysts, and tumors. Being diagnosed with these lumps of cells can be quite scary, but think of them as the body's way of battling with the EBV. Additionally, keep in mind that cancerous tumors result from a combination of EBV and toxins, so treatment must be targeted against both of them.

- Metabolism problems can also tell us whether we're infected by the EBV or not. Related symptoms include mystery weight gain or loss, and being constantly hungry. A more detailed discussion on metabolism is discussed in part two of this book.

- Patients also report experiencing sleep issues. These problems include insomnia, restlessness, fatigue, tiredness, anxiety, and changes in energy levels. Since sleep is a vital element to guarantee our full recovery, part four of this book is entirely dedicated towards addressing our sleep issues and helping us overcome them.

- The EBV is also known to affect our neurotransmitters, which can cause patients to experience numbness, tingles, spasms, and twitches.

- Other notable symptoms of viral infections include an inability to concentrate, memory loss, heightened sensitivity to changing temperatures, fluctuating body temperatures, being extremely moody and irritable, and edema.

With all these symptoms, it would be easier for experts to determine where the EBV is, what kind of strand it is, and at what stage it is. This would greatly help them in preparing a treatment, which would effectively kill of the virus. Only then can we be on the true path to recovery.

Thyroid Cancer

Cancer is probably the worst kind of disease a person can suffer from, and much of our fear of cancer can be attributed to the fact that it still remains a mystery. In this chapter, the author gives us the lowdown on the thyroid cancer virus.

The author believes that the disease is formed when EBV feeds off toxins, thereby creating mutated strains of EBV, which is responsible or the formation of cancer. These mutated EBV continues to feed off toxins and viral byproducts which makes it stronger as it keeps on mutating. This cycle goes on until these virus cells produce a chemical compound, which transforms them into cancer cells. These cancer cells know that they have a better chance for survival when they're clustered together, which explains why cancer is often accompanied by a diagnosis involving bodily tumors.

However, being infected with the EBV doesn't mean that you're already experiencing thyroid cancer. The author reminds us that only certain groups of EBV can cause cancer cells to form, and even if we did get infected, it still requires exposure to a significant amount of toxins in order to form.

From the foregoing, the author now concludes that we only have two major steps to take in order to gain control of our life:

1. To lower our viral load;

2. To effectively eliminate exposure to, and ingestion of, toxins.

In addition, fortunately, this book provides us with various advice, which can help us incorporate the abovementioned steps into our day-to-day life.

Thyroid Guess Tests

The author starts this chapter by discussing the two types of doctors. The first type, or the traditional doctors, are the ones who diagnose a patient based on the latter's thyroid-stimulating hormone (TSH) levels. These levels determine whether a person's thyroid is fine or not depending on the TSH range their results fall under. On the other hand, the second type of doctors acknowledges that even when a person's TSH levels are on the normal range, they still experience thyroid issues. Because of this, they tend to investigate deeper about the disease.

However, even with the presence of the second type of doctors, we can't seem to move forward because the tools used – the thyroid tests – are still outdated. The author explains that our current thyroid tests are focused on the idea that we experience health issues because our thyroid is "sick". However, as previously discussed, our thyroid is perfectly fine – it is the EBV that's causing all the problems.

With this thought, the author encourages the development of tests, which are geared towards detecting EBV. These tests should be able to track where the virus is, where it has traveled to, where it has rested during its dormant phase, whether it has already mutated or not, and what and how it feeds.

For this reason, the author shares two useful tests to help us determine the presence of EBV in our body:

1. Thyroid hormone tests determine the amount of T4, T3, and TSH present in a person's body. When a person's thyroid hormones are below the normal level, it could be a sign that there is a virus infection in our system. The problem with these tests is the possible inaccuracy due to a person's changing hormonal levels. As a tip, the author encourages getting tested several times in a month and getting the average of the results.

2. The author lays more emphasis on the second test, which is the thyroid antibodies test. Our bodies release antibodies to fight off viruses and bacteria, so an increased presence of antibodies should signal us of possible EBV presence.

Keep in mind, however, that these tests are not conclusive as to the absence or presence of pathogens in the entire body. After all, they merely focus on the thyroid. More particularly, they will serve as a guide as to whether or not a person has to take thyroid medication. More on this topic in the next chapter.

Thyroid Medication

When a person is diagnosed with thyroid issues based on traditional testing, they are often prescribed with thyroid medication. However, before you take these medications, it is best to learn more about them in this chapter.

The author shares that current thyroid medication are steroids which help a person to become more energetic, mentally alert, and experience better sleep. However, all these experiences are merely temporary, and do not really address the viral issue. Thus, the temporary relief merely makes the patient forget the fact that a virus is taking over his body. This explains why long-term symptoms, like hair loss and weight gain, still occur despite taking thyroid medication. With that said, the author has likened taking thyroid medication to putting band aid over a deep wound.

It is also worth noting that thyroid medication also has an adverse long-term side effect. The author explains that these steroids train the thyroid to produce less hormones. Over time, and with increasing dosages, the thyroid eventually dumbs itself down and slowly degenerates. Moreover, since the thyroid is the body's data center, then we can only imagine how adverse its effects will be to the body as a whole.

Nonetheless, the author warns us against abruptly stopping thyroid medication. Instead, he encourages us to slowly wean off the medication to avoid shocking the liver and other organs, which work hand-in-hand with the prescription. It is highly advised to talk to your doctor about your plan to go into detox, so that he can prescribe lower dosages over time.

PART II:

The Great Mistakes in Your

Way

A Bridge to Better Health

The second part of this book deals with the various mistakes, which provides a gap on our road to recovery. Fortunately, these gaps are not the dead-end type, which leaves us with no recourse. Bridges can be built on these gaps, and we can use these bridges in order to improve our overall health.

Before beginning the discussion under Part II of this book, the author reminds us that mistakes are a normal part of life. It is so ingrained in our daily life that it is already considered as a normal human experience. In addition, as the saying goes: we learn from our mistakes.

The Great Mistakes under Part II of this book, however, are not the same as our ordinary, day-to-day mistakes. The author likens these Great Mistakes to grave mistakes – mistakes that we are not accountable for, but we have to pay for them nonetheless. The author identified nine Great Mistakes, all of which will be discussed in detail in the succeeding chapters.

Understanding these grave mistakes and building a bridge on them helps us realize that the chronic illnesses we're suffering from is not our own doing. We are not to blame for how our body reacts. Once we ease up to that thought, then we can finally learn to trust ourselves. Moreover, with that self-trust and love, then we can finally begin our journey to improve our health.

Great Mistake 1: Autoimmune Confusion

A common misconception about thyroid problems is that it is caused by an autoimmune response. Unfortunately, this misconception holds us back from obtaining reliable data from research sources since we're focused on the wrong things. Thus, it is for this reason that the author aims to debunk the age-old autoimmune theory.

According to this theory, the body is attacking itself because it has sensed the thyroid as a foreign element, which it must fight off. The truth, however, is that the virus has burrowed deep into the gland, and it is this same virus that the body is attacking – not the thyroid gland itself.

Unfortunately, tests being run at this point are not geared towards detecting these harmful pathogens. According to the author, tests which are specifically made to detect these pathogens have not yet been invented.

Nevertheless, it is advised for patients and medical practitioners alike to acknowledge that the body is not attacking itself. When patients are notified that their body is having an autoimmune response, they end up feeling betrayed by their own body. In effect, they feel helpless and lose interest in trying to heal. This should never be the case.

To conclude, the author lays emphasis on being honest with the patient. Always keep in mind that acknowledging the viral issue not only helps the patient regain control of his body, but will also help you in finding the appropriate cure.

Great Mistake 2: Mystery Illness Misconception

The second great mistake is the mystery illness misconception. We tend to associate mystery illnesses with the rare ailments contracted by children in far-flung areas. The author, however, does not believe in this view.

According to the author, a "mystery illness" is an ailment, which leaves people with more questions than answers. This means that patients and doctors alike are left in the dark about the results of the diagnosis. Usually, these mystery illnesses have no name; nonetheless, there are also instances when named illnesses possess the same mysterious quality. In fact, there are about 5,000 health issues, which are considered as mystery illnesses.

However, the problem doesn't lie in the fact that EBV-related illnesses are considered as mystery illnesses. Instead, it lies in the fact that we're stuck with a broken system – a system that's afraid of not knowing the answers. They fear that if they can't answer questions, their credibility will be damaged; thus, they resort to means which will keep patients from asking questions.

To conclude this chapter, the author encourages us that the first step towards addressing this mistake is to acknowledge that certain illnesses and diseases remain a mystery to us. Once we acknowledge this as a fact, we begin to ignite an awareness among the public, which can also inspire them to help look for answers.

Great Mistake 3: Labels as Answers

The third great mistake is our reliance on labels as the answer to our problems. We often feel relieved when we find out that what we're experiencing has a name, especially when that label is known to be treatable.

The author, however, believes that this reliance on labels makes us docile, which is quite problematic. He explains that once we're diagnosed with a condition that has a name, we rarely ask about it. We're no longer curious about how we caught it in the first place, or what its effects are on our overall health.

This mentality is highly discouraged for two reasons. First keep in mind that misdiagnosis can happen; being a mystery to the medical community means that may be beyond the scope of testing. Second, the label given to these diagnoses don't give us the answers we need. Keep in mind that these diseases are named after who discovered them, but that doesn't always mean that the discovery had an accompanying remedy.

In the alternative, if you were diagnosed with a disease, which made you feel helpless, keep in mind that it is just a label, and not a full disclosure of what you're suffering from. Don't be bogged down by labels.

Great Mistake 4: Inflammation as Cause

Health-related publications are replete with information attributing chronic illnesses to inflammation. Because of this misconception, we were advised to add anti-inflammatory food into our diet, and avoid those, which are inflammatory like grain and processed goods.

However, there are people well over their nineties who eat grains on a daily basis, and are still perfectly healthy. This simply goes to show that inflammation should not be seen as a cause, but as an indicator of an underlying infection or injury. After all, inflammation is a result of an invasion of pathogens like EBV, shingles, or streptococcus, to name a few.

The author shares that because of this misconception, experts tend to focus on testing the levels of inflammation in a person's body and put a label on it based on what disease it is most similar to. Unfortunately, this method makes these tests inconclusive of what you are suffering from.

Additionally, the author also shares that research laboratories merely come up with charts, which assign diseases to particular levels of inflammation. These charts help them analyze blood samples, but it doesn't help them test for the pathogens themselves. In addition, without knowing that the body is infected with pathogens, there is no way of knowing the identity of the specific pathogen – something which is crucial to the patient's treatment.

From the foregoing facts, the author shares that whenever we are diagnosed with an inflammation, we must keep in mind that it is a result of having a pathogenic invader in our body. This will help us accept that our body is not destroying itself. In turn, this will help us develop a positive perspective about our overall health – and only then can we be on the path to true recovery.

Great Mistake 5: Metabolism Myth

Whenever we hear the word "metabolism", we always associate it with the speed by which our body is able to digest the food we eat. We have come to acknowledge that we were born with fast metabolism, which eventually slows down as we age. However, this is all a myth.

According to the author, metabolism simply refers to the fact that the body is alive, and that it is capable of digesting food and convert it to energy. This fact, and the speed by which our body performs these acts, remains the same regardless of age. Nonetheless, metabolism has always been associated with weight gain – even though no explanation has ever been offered to prove it.

Thus, the author feels the responsibility to shatter this metabolism myth and provide us with facts. According to him, weight issues have nothing to do with age nor calories. Instead, it has something to do with our vital organs: the liver, the lymphatic system, heart, pituitary gland, kidney, and intestines.

When our body encounters a virus, both the liver and the lymphatic system slows down. Since these organs are responsible for the detoxification processes, slowing them down meant the continued presence of harmful toxins in the body. As an emergency protective measure, the body thereby retains fluids so that toxins would remain suspended. Thus, we experience weight gain.

From this explanation, we can see that weight gain has more to do with infections, and nothing to do with metabolism. However, since the metabolism myth has been in existence since time immemorial, the author recognizes that it may be hard for us to accept his proposal. Nonetheless, he reminds us that full recovery is achieved only when we let go of burdensome misconceptions.

Great Mistake 6: Gene Blame Game

Another Great Mistake that's hard to swallow is that chronic illnesses are genetic. True enough, we inherit some traits from our parents; but the author believes that we do not get chronic illnesses from them.

In this chapter, the author shares that our bodies are naturally geared towards being healthy. But, if we believe that chronic diseases are inherited – and correlate it to the fact that people suffering from these diseases have quadrupled over the past years – then it would mean that our genes are evolving for the worst. This simply runs counter to the fact that we are meant to be born healthy.

According to the author, what's really inherited are the pathogens – and not faulty genes. Additionally, we must also consider that family members live in the same environment, and are therefore exposed to the same triggers. This explains why family members have the same illnesses. Older members simply develop symptoms earlier because the virus had already been in their bodies for a longer period of time.

Thus, what causes a person to be sick is a compromised immune system, which may either be due to environmental

147

exposure to pathogens or due to contracting them at conception. It has nothing to do with a genetic mutation, which has been passed down from generation to generation.

Great Mistake 7: Ignoring the Unforgiving Four

The author lays much emphasis on the Unforgiving Four. According to him, these four factors are the real problems behind developing chronic diseases. Unfortunately, most of us tend to ignore these factors, which, accordingly, is a grave mistake. The Unforgiving Four are as follows:

1. Radiation. Radiation as a health threat is often ignored, simply because the numbers attributing diseases to it are minimal. Nonetheless, it must be noted that radiation can overheat the thyroid gland, which can also cause the immune system to weaken. In addition, when our immune system is weak, EBV can easily take over.

2. Viral explosion. As previously discussed, most of our diseases are due to viruses; and when these pathogens are coupled with toxins, it can trigger the worst forms of diseases. What's worse, however, is the fact that these viruses can mutate into more hazardous pathogens when they are not properly treated. Thus, there is a need for the medical

community to focus on fighting off these viruses for the long run, instead of just temporary solutions.

3. Dichlorodiphenyltrichloroethane (DDT). DDT used to be a popular component of pesticides, but has been discontinued due to its adverse effects on the environment. Additionally, exposure to this substance can also weaken the immune system and break down our liver. Unfortunately, although its use has already been discouraged, its traces still remain afloat today.

4. Toxic heavy metals. In a previous chapter, the author discussed that the EBV feeds on toxic heavy metals. Thus, exposure to these metals can promote the EBV's development in our body.

All of these may seem too overwhelming and scary. Fortunately, gaining knowledge about the Unforgiving Four can also help us in avoiding them.

Great Mistake 8: It's All in Your Head

Perhaps the worst part of being sick is that it can make you feel like life is unfair. You begin to question what you've done wrong to contract this disease, while you watch your friends proceed with their normal lives. This feeling is especially true when what you've contracted is a chronic disease.

To make matters worse, not much is known about certain chronic illnesses that even the medical community is left hanging. People with good intentions often try to help by saying, "it's all in your head." However, this is doing more bad than good.

Being told that what you're feeling is "all in your head" can be quite frustrating. In certain cases, the frustration becomes too extreme that some patients would go to a psychiatrist to search for answers. Patients eventually lose their self-confidence, and this can be straining to their relationships.

The author admits that this idea can hurt everyone – the patient, his doctor, and his loved ones. Being told that what they're feeling is all a product of their imagination can cause patients to withdraw from looking for answers. This should never be the case.

Great Mistake 9: You Created Your Illness

The final Great Mistake is attributing that your illnesses are manifestations of your thoughts. The author wants to set things straight at the onset of this chapter: your thoughts are not to blame for your illness. Keep in mind that when we entertain the idea that our sufferings are manifestations of our thoughts, then we also limit the control we have over our lives.

To help us realize that believing in this idea is a great mistake, the author gives us an example of a perfectly healthy person who is always bogged down by negative thoughts. In contrast, there are also people who are suffering from chronic illnesses, but who nonetheless possess a positive outlook. He explains that, no matter how negative our thoughts can be, they can never magically transform into a deadly tumor.

At this point, the author wants to emphasize that what truly makes us sick are the pathogens and toxins, which make their way into our bodies. Accepting this can help us rest easy, knowing that we can never conjure up a deadly disease with our thoughts.

Additionally, the author also discourages parents from

developing this mindset among children. This will not only help them grow into worry-free adults, but it can also change the way the next generation will think about chronic diseases.

PART III:

Thyroid Resurrection

Time to Rebuild Your Body

The third part of this book shares various tips on how we can restore the body to its full functionality - and it all starts with taking care of our thyroid.

At this point, we already know that our true enemy is the EBV. Thus, our efforts must be geared towards eliminating it. Nonetheless, the author makes it clear that we shouldn't get rid of all EBV cells in our body. He reassures us that this will not have any adverse effect, since the purpose of the remaining dormant EBV cells is to keep the immune system alert.

The tips listed down in the succeeding chapters are especially relevant to those who received iodine treatments, or those who even had their thyroid glands removed. However, this does not prevent anyone from doing so, especially if they wish to protect their thyroid from any potential threat.

We must also keep in mind that thyroid resurrection is a long journey. We won't see the results in an instant. Nevertheless, with patience and constant efforts, we will eventually experience the positive results of this project.

Life without a Thyroid

It is not uncommon for some people to have their thyroid removed or treated to the point of rendering it seemingly useless. However, in these instances, it can be said that the thyroid is still performing its functions since the body still believes that your thyroid is still wholly intact.

To explain, the author shares that although we've had our thyroid surgically removed, part of it still remains. In other words, the foundation of your thyroid gland is still attached. Additionally, studies reveal that even if we're only left with just one percent of the entire thyroid tissue, this is still enough to produce decent amounts of T4, T3, R5, and R6 hormones which are necessary for the body's full functionality.

Fortunately, we can rebuild our thyroid from the remaining tissue. This is a necessary step towards our full recovery, not just because it can help us produce more hormones, but because it also reduces the adrenals' production of EBV triggers.

You may find, however, that the thought of resurrecting our thyroid is impossible. Nevertheless, the author shares that our thyroid tissue is fully capable of regenerating over time. All that is required of us is to get into the mindset of being healed in order to obtain the best results.

Common Misconceptions and What to Avoid

In this chapter, the author lists down what we have to take note of if we want to experience the full effects of recovery. Among them are the following:

- Avoid iodine. Although iodine is known to be an effective anti-viral and anti-bacterial agent, it can lead to inflammation, which can be easily mistaken as an autoimmune response.

- Avoid the wrong kind of zinc. Although zinc deficiency can awaken a dormant EBV, taking in the wrong kind of zinc also has adverse effects. Research reveals that having too much zinc in the body leads to mineral copper loss, and that can take a toll on our health. The author recommends drinking liquid zinc sulfate, which not only helps us avoid zinc deficiency, but also targets and eliminates toxic copper from our system.

- There is no such thing as goiter-causing food. The belief that certain fruits and vegetables are goitrogenic is a myth. The truth, however, is that the thyroid relies on these food in order to be fully functional. This includes kale, cauliflower, cabbage, pears, peaches, and strawberries, to name a few.

- As much as possible, try to avoid food which are also considered as the EBV's favorite snacks. Food such as eggs, cheese, milk, butter, cream, gluten, canola, non-organic corn, soy, and pork.

It is normal to feel discouraged after looking at the long list of food to avoid. We must keep in mind that we do not have to stop eating all of these at once. We can gradually remove them from our diet so that the transition will not be as hard for us. The author also provides us with suggested recipes, which will be discussed in succeeding chapters.

Powerful Foods, Herbs, and Supplements for Healing

Now that we already have an idea of what we should avoid, the author now presents us with a longer list of food and supplements, which we can eat. Our body needs nourishment, after all.

- Artichokes contain phytochemical compounds, which aids the restoration of the thyroid gland itself. Additionally, these compounds can help shrink tumors, so that the EBVs hiding inside them are directly exposed to our immune system. Other food, which contain phytochemicals, include basil and avocadoes.

- Aloe Vera gel is an antiviral food, which can help flush out toxins from the bloodstream. Other antiviral food include thyme, radish, garlic, fennel, coconut, and basil.

- Apples and asparagus contain anti-inflammatory properties which starves the virus, thereby preventing it from reproducing.

- Atlantic sea vegetables like dulse and kelp contain the right amount of iodine, which serves as an antiseptic for the thyroid.

- Food rich in hydrochloric acid and calcium blocks the EBV from further damaging the thyroid. This includes lime, lemon, orange, tangerine, and papaya.

- Tomatoes and papaya contain high levels of vitamin C, which helps cleanse the liver. It also provides additional support to the thyroid's own immune system.

- Sprouts and microgreens contain micronutrients, which reduces and prevents the growth of harmful nodules.

- Cruciferous vegetables like broccoli, cauliflower, and cabbage are rich in sulfur content, which renders the virus incapable of performing its functions.

- Other food which help in the restoration and growth of thyroid tissues include turmeric, watercress, wild blueberries, sweet potatoes, squash, spinach, raw honey, and potatoes.

- Aside from the food listed above, it is also important to take the necessary supplements, which can speed up the healing process, like vitamin B12, liquid zinc sulfate, vitamin C, l-lysine. 5-methyltetrahydrofoolate, monolaurin, silver hydrosol, l-tyrosine, b-complex, magnesium, eicosapentaenoic acid, docosahexaenoic acid, selenium, curcumin, chromium, vitamin D, manganese, copper, and rubidium.

- Helpful herbs include spirulina, cat's claw, licorice root, lemon balm, chaga mushroom, star anise, bacopa monnieri, red clover, elderberry, bladder wrack, nettle leaf, red marine algae, ashwagandha, and barley grass. These herbs are either rich in phytochemicals, or contain antiviral properties which can effectively target the EBV.

90-Day Thyroid Rehab

At this point, we now have a list of both the EBV-friendly and EBV-destroying foods. In this chapter, the author encourages us to go on a 90-day cleanse using his carefully-prepared meal plans.

The author has prepared three choices for us, each of which would be sufficient for a 30-day period. We are also given the option to mix and match the plans in order to determine which one would be most effective, depending on our particular needs. Recipes for these meals will be discussed in the next chapter.

Choice A: Liver, Lympphatic, and Gut Release Month

In choice A, you start the morning by drinking 16 ounces of celery juice. This must be done on an empty stomach. At midday or in the afternoon, you drink around 16 ounces of lemon or lime water. In the late afternoon, drink another 16 ounces of lemon or lime water. Finally, you end the night with 16 ounces of aloe water or cucumber juice.

During this period, try to remove eggs, dairy, gluten, canola, corn, soy, and pork from your diet. This plan works since your busy organs are given additional support, while the antiviral properties also attacks the EBV in your system.

Choice B: Heavy Metal Detox Month

Start the day by drinking 16 ounces of celery juice. For thirty days, you must drink the heavy metal detox smoothie for breakfast. At midday or early afternoon, drink 16 ounces of lime or lemon water. In the late afternoon, drink 16 ounces of ginger water. Then, in the evening, drink around 16 ounces of aloe water or cucumber juice. As an alternative in case you don't have access to these ingredients, you can opt to drink lemon water instead.

Just like in Choice A, try to avoid the unproductive food like eggs and cheese. Additionally, avoid tuna, swordfish, and bass during this period.

Choice C: Thyroid Virus Cleanse Month

While still on an empty stomach, drink 16 ounces of celery juice in the morning. For breakfast, drink the thyroid healing smoothie. At midday or early afternoon, drink around 16 ounces of lemon or lime water. Within the day, drink one cup of ginger water, and then one cup of thyroid healing tea. During dinner, or at any time, drink at least one cup of thyroid healing broth. Finally, drink at least 16 ounces of thyroid healing juice every evening.

In addition to the prohibitions in the previous chapter, you must also reduce your fat intake by around 25 percent. It is advised to have only one portion of animal protein per day during this month.

Thyroid Healing Recipes

In this chapter, the author lays down his recommended recipes for the meals mentioned in the previous chapters. These recipes have been categorized into juices, teas & broth, breakfast, lunch, dinner, and snacks.

Juices, Tea, Waters & Broth

- Thyroid healing juice. For this juice, you will need one bunch of celery, two apples, one bunch of cilantro, and two to four inches of fresh ginger. Thoroughly clean all these ingredients and run them though the juicer. As much as possible, use all-organic ingredients.

- Thyroid healing tea. You will need two cups of water, one teaspoon thyme, one teaspoon fennel seed, one teaspoon lemon balm, and two teaspoons of raw honey. Bring the water to a boil, then add thyme, fennel seed, and lemon balm. Turn of the water and allow to cool for around fifteen minutes. Add honey to taste.

- Ginger water. You need 1 to 2 inches of fresh ginger,

two cups of water, half a lemon, and two teaspoons of raw honey. Begin by grating the ginger into the water, and add the juice of the lemon. Leave the water for at least 15 minutes, or you can put it in the fridge overnight Add honey or lemon to add to the taste before drinking.

- Aloe water. You will need a 2-inch piece of fresh and organic aloe leaf and two cups of water. Place the scooped out aloe gel and water into a blender and blend until thoroughly mixed.

- Thyroid healing broth. You will need two sliced sweet potatoes, two celery stalks, two onions, six garlic cloves, one inch turmeric root, one cup of chopped parsley, four sprigs of thyme, two tablespoons of Atlantic dulse flakes, one tablespoon of kelp powder, and eight cups of water. Mix all these ingredients into a boil, and then simmer for around an hour.

Breakfast

- Apple porridge with cinnamon and raisins. You will need three sliced apples, a quarter teaspoon of cinnamon, one pinch of vanilla bean powder, two pitted dates, one teaspoon of raw honey, half a lemon, a quarter cup of raisins, two tablespoons of walnuts, two tablespoons of shredded coconut. Place all the ingredients in a food processor until all of them are thoroughly mixed. You may opt to add walnuts, coconut, raisins, or raw honey, depending on your desired flavor.

- Heavy metal detox smoothie. You will need two bananas, two cups of wild blueberries, a cup of cilantro, one teaspoon o barley grass juice powder, one teaspoon of Hawaiian spirulina, one tablespoon of Atlantic dulse, one orange, and a cup of water. Mix all of these into a blender and allow to blend until smooth.

- Thyroid healing smoothie. You will need two cups of mango, one banana, and a cup of water. Blend all these ingredients until smooth. You may also add ginger, raspberries, spinach, kelp powder, or arugula, depending on your taste.

Lunch

- Mixed vegetable salad. Layer red cabbage, carrots, asparagus, sliced radish, fennel, celery, cilantro,

169

parsley, scallion, lemon, avocado, spinach, or arugula into a mason jar. Store these vegetables in the fridge for up to three days. Serve this with a salad dressing made from blended brazil nuts, cashews, celery, garlic, parsley, dill, celery seeds, sea salt, lemon, and water.

- Fruit salad with leafy greens. Layer oranges, raspberries, mangoes, cucumber, pomegranate seeds, cilantro, basil, lime, and leafy greens into a mason jar. Allow to chill in the fridge for up to three days, and serve with freshly squeezed lemon juice.

- Spinach soup. You will need one and a half cup of grape tomatoes, one talk of celery, one garlic clove, one orange, four cups of baby spinach, two basil leaves, and half an avocado. Begin by blending the tomatoes, celery, garlic, and orange juice. Once smooth, add the spinach until it is completely incorporated into the soup. At your option, you may add basil and avocado to add to the taste.

Dinner

- Steamed artichokes with garlic cashew aioli. Steam the artichokes for around 30 to 40 minutes. While steaming, combine cashews, olive oil, garlic, lemon juice, sea salt, and water into a blender to create a thick aioli. Serve the artichokes with the aioli.

- Cauliflower "fried rice". Put cauliflower into a food processor until it reaches a rice-like texture. Sauté onion, ginger, garlic, carrot, bell pepper, celery, and peace into a pan with one teaspoon of coconut oil. When you notice the vegetables soften, add the coauliflower rice, toasted sesame oil, coconut aminos, honey, and sea salt. Stir well until the cauliflower rice is tender.

Snacks

- Wild blueberry banana ice cream. Put three large frozen bananas and a cup of wild blueberries into a food processor, and pulse until it creates a soft-serve ice cream consistency. Place one cup of wild blueberries into a food processor to create the sauce.

- The author also recommends the "grab and go" snack combos of: cauliflower and apples, tomatoes and spinach, celery and dates, banana and dulse flakes, kale and mango, pears and arugula, wild blueberries and papaya, and tangerine and raspberries.

Thyroid Healing Techniques

Now that we have been acquainted with the various thyroid healing recipes, the author now presents us with thyroid healing techniques which will complement our new diet.

1. The first technique is called the Light Infusion Tonics. You begin this technique by pouring a glass of water and setting it in front of you. Raise your hand above your head and curl it into a fist. As your hand is raised, visualize that it is filling with white light. Open your hand and point your fingers toward the glass and say, "light" out loud. Visualize that the light from your hands is streaming towards the water. Do this procedure for a total of seven times. According to the author, this will turn the water into a divine, transformative tonic. Gargle this water before swallowing it, and make sure to visualize that the water is effectively killing the EBV cells in your thyroid.

2. The second technique is called the Butterfly Sun Soaking. The author shares that the shape of our thyroid is similar to that of a butterfly. Moreover, just

like the wings of a butterfly, our thyroid is capable of storing and collecting sunlight. In order to do so, we must try to soak up as much sunlight and direct it into our neck area where our thyroid is located. Exposure to sunlight works since it not only balances our body's hormone production, but it also powers up our thyroid while preventing the EBV from reproducing.

3. The final technique encourages us to ask for support from people with healthy thyroid glands. The author explains that our thyroid can produce radio-like frequencies, which can be detected by another person's thyroid. Thus, when a healthy thyroid receives signals from an ailing thyroid, the former also sends out a healing signal to help the latter recover. For best results, make sure that you are standing not more than an arm's length apart from each other.

Finally Healed – One Woman's Story

In this chapter, the author shares the story of Sally Arnold, a person who once suffered from thyroid problems. The author proudly shares Sally's story, because it is a proof that the recipes and techniques listed in this book are effective in thyroid resurrection.

Sally is a registered nurse who is passionate about helping people with their health. Ironically, she was also experiencing her own health challenges, which required her to undergo hormone replacement therapy in as early as her 20s. Unfortunately, the symptoms stayed with her despite taking medication and getting therapy, and it went on until she was in her 50s. This eventually led her to contact the author to ask for help.

The author advised Sally to begin by cutting down the problematic food discussed under Chapter 21. She was also advised to load up on fruits and vegetables, while taking up antiviral supplements. Little by little, this change in her diet helped Sally feel better.

Sally eventually became convinced that she needed to stop

her thyroid medication, so she decided to gradually lower her prescriptions. Within months of being medicine-free, Sally happily reported that her TSH level is now within the normal range, which proves that the diet is an effective way to tame the EBV in her system.

After two years, Sally has fully embrace the thyroid resurrection diets and techniques discussed in this book. Currently, she no longer experiences panic attacks, constipation, back pains, and other autoimmune symptoms. She also noticed that her thyroid nodules, as well as the fungal growth in her toenails, were no longer there.

Nevertheless, Sally shares that the biggest difference – and her greatest relief – was the improvement in her mental state. She shares that after she has fully embraced the lifestyle embodied in this book, she became overwhelmed by a sense of well-being. She no longer felt anxious and exhausted. She was finally happy and at peace.

From Sally's story, we can see that it is perfectly possible to rebuild the thyroid. Change is possible if we know how to do so. Fortunately, this book has all the answers.

Part IV:

Secrets of Sleep

Insomnia and Your Thyroid

In the fourth and final part of this book, the author discusses the relationship between insomnia and our thyroid. Although emphasis must be placed on the fact that thyroid issues do not cause insomnia, sleep is nonetheless important in the healing process.

There are various reasons why we experience insomnia, but a thyroid issue is not one of them. It may be because of an MSG buildup in our brain, or a clogged liver, or that you are experiencing pains from the EBV's neurotoxins.

The author recognizes that not getting enough sleep is quite stressful. Fortunately, there are ways, which can help give you better sleep. To get us interested, the author lists down the following reasons why we should continue reading the next chapters:

1. We will be able to determine what is causing our sleepless nights, and once we know what's behind the issue, then treatment will no longer be a mystery.

2. There are sleep secrets which we can use in order to fast-track our healing process.

Your Sleep Wellspring

Sleep remains a mystery, even to the medical community. Nonetheless, the author believes that only one thing is certain: that we all deserve sleep. Laying emphasis on this fact is at the heart of this chapter.

The author explains that sleep is not an ordinary bodily function, but a divine right given to us by the Holy Source. With this in mind, we should never feel guilty for choosing to sleep over working or studying.

Society, however, thinks otherwise. Society demands too much time from us that we often end up being sleep-deprived. On the other hand, those who would always choose sleep are often labeled as lazy or have no goals in life.

Because of this stigma, a majority of the population end up developing sleep issues. However, since sleep is such a medical mystery, science reveals no concrete answers yet.

Fortunately, there are solid laws of sleep, which will help us take the first step in addressing our sleep issues. The heart of these laws revolve around the fact that we have the fundamental right to sleep. The laws of sleep are as follows:

1. We have a sleep wellspring. According to this law, we earn two seconds of sleep with every breath we take. Think of it as an unlimited sleep supply, which we're all entitled to simply because we're alive. Additionally, this sleep wellspring is being guarded by both the Holy Source and the Earthly Mother, so you are assured that it will never run out. Thus, keep this law in mind whenever you feel like you didn't get enough sleep.

2. We have the power to allow ourselves to sleep. Having an unlimited sleep supply is only one part of the equation; the other part lies in giving ourselves the permission to enjoy it. The author shares that whenever we start to feel guilty about going to sleep, remind yourself that you are entitled to sleep as a matter of right, and no one can ever take that away from you.

Now that we're acquainted with these laws, we finally ease up to the idea of getting more sleep. Once we feel more relaxed and entitled to it, and then we can formally begin with assessing and identifying our sleep issues.

Identifying Sleep Issues

We won't have a concrete answer to our problems if we don't know what these problems are in the first place. In this chapter, the author recognizes that there are various sleep issues caused by different factors. To help us determine our specific sleep issue, he lists down the common issues as follows:

- The inability to sleep after hours of tossing around in bed, then feeling restless as soon as you wake up.

- You often wake up in the wee hours of the morning, and then experience an inability to go back to sleep. You end up feeling frustrated and anxious as the sun starts to rise.

- You easily fall asleep, but wake up late at night. Unlike the previous problem, you eventually fall back to sleep, but it is already in the morning.

- You never enter the REM stage of sleep since you are in and out of bed, which is often accompanied by frequent trips to the comfort room to urinate.

- You are completely awake at night, which eventually

leaves you without energy throughout the day.

- You feel exhausted throughout the day, which makes you excited to end the day and sleep. However, as soon as nighttime falls, you are completely awake.

- You experience a full night's sleep, but it doesn't feel like it's enough. Then, you get a report from your loved ones that you're either loudly snoring or shallowly breathing. In certain instances, you won't be told that you have breathing issues, but you do feel an overwhelming exhaustion which persists throughout the day – despite sleeping for about eight hours.

- You are about to fall asleep, but you experience the sudden jerk of your arm or leg, which jolts you up. This happens several times in the course of your sleep.

- You feel exhausted and ready to sleep, but your mind or body seems to be experiencing sensations, which keeps you awake, like racing thoughts, restless legs syndrome, or tinnitus.

Now that we're acquainted with these common sleep issues,

we should now be acquainted with the top causes of sleep. The author lists them down as follows:

1. Viral activity causes hypersensitivity in our central nervous system, which keeps us alert at night.

2. Exposure to toxic heavy metals shuts down our neurotransmitters, which prevents it from sending sleep messages throughout the brain.

3. High MSG intake can also cause your nervous system to become hypersensitive. MSG is a known neuron antagonist, and it can easily derail the brain's normal activities when taken in large amounts.

4. A sluggish liver due to high intake of fatty and processed food. Keep in mind that our liver also takes its rest when we sleep, but it fails to do so whenever we eat a lot of unhealthy food. Because of this, our liver works hard even when we're asleep, and that churning can cause a disturbance in the body which eventually keeps us awake.

5. Digestive issues like bloating, cramping, or a sensitive stomach keeps the nervous system alert, which also explains how these issues can trigger sleeplessness.

6.   Failure to let go of emotional wounds and traumatic experiences.

7.   Sleep apnea, which results from a combination of MSG toxicity and heavy metal exposure, can cause blockages in our airways during sleep. Unfortunately, these blockages cause a chemical imbalance in the brain, which eventually leads to a feeling of exhaustion in the morning.

8.   Adrenal fatigue, which means that your adrenaline is underactive during the day, but is hyperactive at night. This causes you to feel suddenly awake despite feeling exhausted throughout the day.

9.   Being anxious can also cause the brain to become hyperactive. Unfortunately, anxiety can be triggered by a lot of factors, including being fearful, nervous, having high degrees of DDT in the brain, or experiencing digestive problems.

Healing Sleep Issues

Now that we've identified our sleep issues, we can now proceed to healing them. In this chapter, the author provides us with a list of targeted solutions for each sleep issue.

- For those dealing with viral infection, high exposure to heavy metals, MSG toxicity, other toxin overload, the first step is to detoxify the body. Refer to the chapter on the 90-day Thyroid Rehab to get started.

- Those experiencing sluggish liver, adrenal fatigue, and digestive liver, make sure to take in more of the healing food and herbs discussed in previous chapters, and avoid the unproductive ones like eggs and dairy products.

- Those experiencing adrenal fatigue are encouraged to remove adrenalized food from their diets. This not only makes you healthier, but it also calms down your adrenal glands so that you can finally enjoy a good night's sleep.

- For digestive issues, the author recommends eating food rich in probiotics and vitamin B12. These are

184

supplements, which are known to help and improve our digestive system.

- For obstructive sleep apnea, make sure to get a dose of food rich in l-glutamine, 5-HTP, melatonin, magnesium l-threonate, glycine, and magnesium glycinate. This includes mangoes, wild blueberries, garlic, cilantro, sweet potatoes, lettuce, celery, spinach, asparagus, bananas, and cherries.

- In addition, for those who are always anxious, calm yourself down with an herbal tea brew made of raw honey, sweet potato, and avocado.

Why Bad Dreams Are Good

In some instances, the main cause for lack of sleep is having bad dreams. These dreams tend to be so vivid and memorable that we'd rather not go back to sleep out of fear that it will have the same horrible dream.

However, in this chapter, the author makes us realize that bad dreams are actually good for us. In fact, he shares that these dreams indicate that our system is fully operational. These bad dreams, he theorizes, are the soul's way of healing itself.

He explains that throughout the day, we have emotional walls up which serve as a filter for all these negative emotions. As we sleep, the brain is finally given the chance to process these emotions, and when the brain gets busy, these negative emotions begin to manifest through our sleep. Instead of looking at this process from a negative perspective, think of it in this way: that it is our body's own way of releasing these emotions. Without being able to release them, these emotions will pile up in our system, and can become troublesome in the long run.

Of course, this doesn't mean that having good dreams is bad for you. Having good dreams means that you are experiencing a lot of positive emotions throughout your day, so there's nothing to worry about.

To conclude, experiencing vivid dreams – whether good or bad – is perfectly normal and healthy. These dreams are neither challenges nor punishments. Instead, they are reminders that you are alive, and that you have a body that's responsive and healthy.

Conclusion

Thyroid problems are quite common. However, despite its seemingly regular occurrence, it is still considered as one of the biggest mysteries of our time. That is, until this book came along.

In this book, the author shares that a common misconception in the medical community is that thyroid problems are caused by an autoimmune response of the body against the gland. They considered these problems as illnesses with their own category, and tried to look for remedies from that standpoint. However, the author shares that these thyroid problems are not standalone illnesses – instead, he proposes that these are symptoms of something bigger going on inside our bodies. In addition, once we come to accept these issues as mere symptoms, we then realize what the real problem is: the thyroid virus.

The thyroid virus, according to the author, is a pathogen also known as the Epstein-Barr virus (EBV) – the same virus, which is responsible for causing mononucleosis. With this identified, shouldn't the treatment for thyroid issues become easier? Unfortunately, this is not always the case.

The author explains that today's tests are not focused on detecting the virus. These tests merely focus on analyzing the patient's thyroid hormone levels, and then make a prescription based on the result. However, since a person's TSH levels fluctuate from time to time, these tests rarely produce accurate results. To make matters worse, thyroid medication is also known to have adverse side effects on some of our vital organs, so it's best to stay away from them as much as possible.

In the second part of the book, the author discusses the nine mistakes that we make – or are made to believe – which blocks us from full thyroid recovery. Among these mistakes include misconceptions about our metabolism, inflammation, and blaming ourselves for our illnesses. However, among these mistakes, the author lays emphasis on ignoring four external factors, which largely contribute to chronic diseases. According to the author radiation, viral explosion, DDT, and toxic heavy metals, are among the items that the EBV loves to feed on. Thus, avoiding them greatly reduces the risk of contracting or waking up a dormant EBV.

With everything discussed, and the fact that the EBV can be extremely powerful, some patients may eventually feel helpless. This is especially disheartening for those who have already had their thyroid glands removed – who, after all, would then be in charge of sending signals to the various organs in the body?

Fortunately, around 30 to 40 percent of the thyroid tissue stays intact, even when the patient is made to believe that it has been completely removed. Even further good news is that the thyroid tissue can still perform its functions despite only being a quarter of its original size. This fact is great news to us because this means that thyroid resurrection is achievable.

To fully rebuild our thyroid, we must avoid the food, which are considered as the EBV's favorites. This includes protein from dairy, eggs, and processed food rich in MSG. Conversely, we must also add EBV-fighting food and supplements into our diet. This includes cabbage, berries, sweet potatoes, magnesium, zinc, and vitamin B12, among others. Nonetheless, an improved diet is only one part of the equation. The other part requires us to adopt thyroid resurrecting techniques and getting enough rest.

Once we learn to live with all these factors, then we can truly say that we are on the path towards healing our thyroid.

FREE BONUSES

P.S. Is it okay if we overdeliver?

Here at Readtrepreneur Publishing, we believe in overdelivering way beyond our reader's expectations. Is it okay if we overdeliver?

Here's the deal, we're going to give you an extremely condensed PDF summary of the book which you've just read and much more…

What's the catch? We need to trust you… You see, we want to overdeliver and in order for us to do that, we've to trust our reader to keep this bonus a secret to themselves? Why? Because we don't want people to be getting our exclusive PDF summaries even without buying our books itself. Unethical, right?

Ok. Are you ready?

Firstly, remember that your book is code: "**READ58**".

Next, visit this link: **http://bit.ly/exclusivepdfs**

Everything else will be self explanatory after you've visited: **http://bit.ly/exclusivepdfs.**

We hope you'll enjoy our free bonuses as much as we enjoyed preparing it for you!